THE MAN FROM HARRODS

THE MAN FROM HARRODS

Steven Harris

The Book Guild Ltd

First published in Great Britain in 2021 by
The Book Guild Ltd
9 Priory Business Park
Wistow Road, Kibworth
Leicestershire, LE8 0RX
Freephone: 0800 999 2982
www.bookguild.co.uk
Email: info@bookguild.co.uk
Twitter: @bookguild

Typeset in 11pt Minion Pro

Printed and bound in the UK by TJ Books LTD, Padstow, Cornwall

ISBN 978 1913551 858

British Library Cataloguing in Publication Data.
A catalogue record for this book is available from the British Library.

For Maria Dimova

CONTENTS

INTRODUCTION

I was a rather naïve youth who, at the age of sixteen, wanted to stay on at school mainly because I had few qualifications (well, I did possess a CSE grade 4 in woodwork!) and had not fully realised that young adults would, pretty soon, have to make their own way in the world.

I lived with my brother and sister, first in Beechholme Children's Home (this Surrey institution had and continued to have a notorious reputation), and later on in the rather space-age town of Stevenage, in Hertfordshire. At least it seemed that way at the time, with its modern housing, town centre and network of cycle paths everywhere. It was a post-war new town, and me and my siblings lived there as part of a foster family of about ten children in all. However, it had apparently been agreed that after my education had finished at Barnwell Comprehensive School, my brother and I would move to London to live with my father.

Work, any work, it seemed, was all I needed so that I could help with the rent. This was the late 1970s, when people could walk relatively easily from one job to another, and the more sensible folk talked about joining big companies: join one of them and you've got a job for life. It was a fairly exciting time even if there were no computers, mobile phones or M25. At least most of us had colour televisions and the new-fangled video recorders.

I didn't enter the piano trade immediately, working in a camping store initially, but if you read on you will see how I (renamed John Turner in this book) almost stumbled into the profession of piano tuning, managing to secure a training – of sorts – with the famous department store Harrods of Knightsbridge. This prestigious emporium, in the Brompton Road, had one Charles Henry Harrod as its founder (in 1849). Before breaking into the world of groceries and tea dealing, he came close to being transported to Tasmania for handling stolen goods. Still, he had been orphaned by the age of thirteen and proved to be an astute businessman.

I never had a job for life at Harrods, but managed to build a fairly sound career in the world of pianos before moving away from Harrods and being completely self-employed. Let me introduce you to some of my customers and experiences...

PLAIN SAILING

MONDAY 27TH JANUARY

10.00am, Mrs Jones

This is what I like. Not too early a start, twenty minutes' drive. Nice upright piano that holds its tuning reasonably well. I'll spend fifty minutes on it and, half-way through, Mrs Jones will bring in a coffee and biscuits. I like it because she knows what I like – brings it in automatic – doesn't sit and expect conversation, so I can keep more or less to time and work in peace and quiet. Why can't all customers be like her? She even has the piano cleared before I arrive.

With some customers I'm expected to clear the piano's top of books (sometimes stacks of them), photographs and heavy lamp-shades. Grand pianos are the worst: dozens of framed photos or, at Christmas or birthdays, cards and presents galore. This takes ten minutes before I can even open the piano and open my case and make a start. In houses where the owner doesn't feel obliged to help me replace the items afterwards (another ten minutes), I've started using the excuse about not being sure in what order the items should go back or I say, "I didn't put them back in case you wanted to have a dust round first." Most women are not sure if I am insinuating that they don't keep a clean house, so they usually reassure me, before changing the subject, that it's fine to leave the things just where they are.

Anyhow, back to Mrs Jones. She even pays in cash – real money, not a cheque – and doesn't want to try the piano. She can't play, it's the children who are having lessons, and she's heard me play a snippet anyway: very impressed. I could see the repertoire and level of her kids' ability by the graded music books she'd taken off the piano (as she'd taken the trouble to take them off, I, of course, ensure they all go back nice and neatly afterwards). From the range of music, it's obvious the children are still at the 'middle of the keyboard/no pedals' stage: most of the notes just won't be used. But I always make sure the pedals are functioning properly (especially no squeaks) and that all the notes are reasonably in tune. In truth, I could have just tuned the middle (and not even have done that very well) and Mrs Jones would have been happy. It's amazing how many piano owners don't know when a piano is out of tune; this includes quite accomplished pianists and music teachers sometimes. Or they only know it's out of tune when it's got to the stage of sounding absolutely horrendous: so bad that when a well-known tune is played on the said piano, it is almost unrecognisable. Rather like only knowing you need a mechanic when the car has stopped and simply won't go any further. I believe in most cases a car warns you before coming to a complete standstill. Usually you are given plenty of warning: a slipping clutch, slightly harder to start first time, spongy brakes.

No, Mrs Jones is not like those customers who test your tuning more out of suspicion than expertise; but I have some sympathy for those who feel they are caught in the 'ordering wine' syndrome. The waiter has put a drop into the glass and you're supposed to go through the tasting routine. You know, hold it up to the light, twirl it around, flared nostrils – everything bar spitting it out. He knows that you know he thinks it's just plonk and that you have probably never even seen a Blue Nun let alone something else in the higher price bracket, but you are both obliged to go through with the ritual. And even if there is a small problem with the wine, you're not going to say anything unless you like being regarded as a stroppy or arrogant bast… let's say basket.

No, I don't mind people trying out the tuning. Occasionally, talented musicians make it all worthwhile, but it's annoying if not sometimes amusing to see customers prodding a key with one finger and listening intently. They sit there with a pained expression (which presumably is supposed to look discerning), asking, "…Uhm, what do you think? Doesn't it need a bit more tweaking?" Not a very technical word, 'tweaking'. Detecting no hint of doubt on my satisfied face, they prod it again, comparing one note with its neighbour. Perhaps it hadn't occurred to them that a G is not supposed to sound like an A. The more idiotic test which some of them seem to have devised for themselves is to play the last notes, the ones at the extreme ends of the piano. They use their left hand to hit the first bass note and, stretching out (temptingly for crucifixion?) with their right hand, aim to hit the top, shrill treble note at the opposite end. Twisting their necks, which I'd quite like to do a bit further in these situations, they look for approval and a second opinion. As if any musician, or I, with five years' training and decades of experience, and having just slogged away on their piano for an hour, would use this as a reliable and sensible test of a piano's tuning. And how many times are those two extreme notes at either end of the piano likely to be played at all (let alone together) in the next six months?

These are the same people who sit listening intently to one note at a time, until the last dregs of its sound have been spirited away, and ask, "Can you hear that?" They ask you again, excitedly repeating the note as though they have discovered a flaw in your work. Questioning them never seems to elicit what, exactly, is the problem. Dejected, they move on and, seemingly reluctantly, eventually hand over the fee some ten minutes later. Perhaps in some cases they are confusing tuning with tone. A piano can be perfectly in tune but sound rather unpleasant. Tone can be improved (a separate job and fee), for example, by working on the shape and surface of the hammer felt, but you can't make a silky instrument out of a pig's bladder. No, some customers see the tuning as a cure-all. But it is simply a routine, methodical process done mechanically to ensure each string is tuned correctly in relation to the others. Which is why it is not absolutely necessary to be able to play the piano in order to be able to tune it (in the same way a mechanic can fix your car without having to know how to drive it). Still, it is better to be able to play at least something on the piano, as otherwise you run the risk of being considered a fraud.

11.15am, Miss McFroude

I don't think Miss McFroude considered me a fraud; it was just that I never stood a chance of being accepted. It was a case of the family doctor being replaced with the new Dr Singh, or whoever. No one is going to match up to Dr Burns, who not only brought you and your mother into the world but probably also your grandmother and eleven of her twelve children too (and the twelfth one never saw more than two months anyway). No, Miss McFroude had had Mr Burns since not long after the war (Boer War, possibly?), and, when he had rather inconsiderately died (piano tuners never retire; they work right up to the last Friday of life and die on the Saturday or Sunday), she'd been forced to find a replacement.

She found me through the librarian's husband's half-sister's part-time saxophone teacher, who had got my number from his next-door neighbour but one. Apparently I had tuned the said next-door neighbour but one's piano just once and they'd been meaning to get me round again as it was going 'a bit off'. I should think it *was* a bit off after all this time: I could vaguely remember doing it two or three years back. That's another couple who don't know when a piano needs tuning!

With Miss McFroude, as soon as she heard my closing arpeggios and rather melodic tune, she wasn't lacking in bluntness: "Oh…" picking up the signal to come in to the room, but with an air of disappointment, continuing, "can't all piano tuners play then? Mr Burns always played beautifully after he had finished, you know. Actually, I'd never let him leave until he'd played the piece by Chopping. It was worth the fee just to hear one of his polla-neices… Marvellous man, so utterly reliable. And always immaculate in his tie and jacket – a real old gentleman." I was a patient man – tuning pianos, by its very nature, requires a good deal of patience – but I'd heard nothing but Mr Burns this and Mr Burns that since I'd entered the house. On removing the front panel in order to get at the tuning pins, I'd carefully stood the panel out of the way, against a wall. "Ooh, that might fall over. Mr Burns always laid it on the floor." Obligingly, I removed it and laid it down in front of the bookcase while Miss McFroude rubbed away imaginary dirt marks from the wall left by the 'careless' piano tuner.

The discussion of the fee had started even earlier, over the phone. Apparently, my fee was a little more than Mr Burns' (or 'dear Mr B', as she called him), who was a very experienced piano tuner. I cancelled this out by mentioning the fact that I had further to travel. I also suspected that Mr B's fee was not wholly declared. Elderly piano tuners are clever enough to retire officially, but keep on favoured cash customers and pass on less favoured ones (presumably there was a Scottish affinity between Miss McF and Mr B). Sometimes such arrangements backfire.

I have heard on more than one occasion about the tax people chasing certain deceased tuners' wives for their late husbands' undeclared earnings. A possible case of tuning the books rather than cooking them?

I'd had no choice over the beverage offered (tea), which appeared after about twenty minutes. Mr Burns always had tea (apparently) and so it was presumably decided that all piano tuners drink tea, but I didn't mind that.

Moving on to the end of the job, the piano having been tuned and it was nearly time to put my tools away and clear up, this final conversation about Mr Burns' playing reminded me of what another mature piano tuner told me what he'd said when he'd come across a similar 'complaint' about him not being a pianist: "Madam, if I was half as good a pianist as I am a piano tuner, I'd be playing in all the concert halls across Europe rather than be standing here talking to you." Should I say this to Miss McFroude (whose name was sounding remarkably like Miss Much-Frown now), I wondered, as she returned to the room and stepped forward to hand over the fee. "There, before you put it up even higher!" Jabbingly, her outstretched hand proffered some crumpled notes. I thought she was going to hit me for a minute, and stepped back to gain some personal space. Over I went, catching my ankle on that confounded piano panel which I hadn't had a chance to put back in. By fluke I managed to land up in the large armchair by the fireplace. There wasn't a trace of dignity left in me as Miss Mc F looked down bemused at the bumbling, over-priced piano tuner who had a lot to learn yet.

Being a relatively young piano tuner didn't seem to hold any advantages. Perhaps partly due to the fact that many piano tuners can work until they literally drop, and as there are few around, they're always in demand. The stereotypical image seems to be that either piano tuners are well past middle-age or they are blind (or both). For me in my twenties, to the customers it must have seemed like the equivalent of parents wishing to see the headmaster of their son's prospective new school and being interviewed by the head boy instead. Being rather baby-faced anyway, I grew a beard to help reassure the customers. Nonetheless, the outcome of a certain promising telephone enquiry was very disappointing. I was tuning a piano for a colleague in his piano restoration workshop. They had a call from a film company who urgently needed a piano tuner to appear briefly in a background scene, while the star waltzed through, deep in thought or conversation, in the foreground. Would I be interested? I told my colleague, "Yes!" Would I be free in a couple of weeks' time? My excitement grew: "Yes!" There followed other routine-type questions between my colleague (now sounding very much like my agent) and the film man until I heard the subject of age crop up: "Oh, about middle twenties, I think." Seconds later the receiver was put down and any thoughts of Turner, the tuner, appearing at the Odeon nationwide were wiped out: a film career tragically cut oh-so-short. I later learnt that my colleague had had to recommend another more matured man in the piano business, a technician who knew his way around the insides of a piano though had little idea how to tune one. He had a short, white beard and craftsman's hands, though, and was snapped up for five minutes of fame simply because he looked like a piano tuner and I didn't.

1.00pm, Mr Armada

Time for a quick lunch then it's over to Mr Armada. I stop at an Italian-run cafe. Like other workers who eat on the hoof, I've become reasonably knowledgeable about eating out in London (and elsewhere) during the day. I'm not too fussy but much prefer home-cooked pies or any home-cooked food to burgers and chips. There are far, far too many cafes nowadays which only serve dull, processed food that is thrown into the hot fryer or destroyed by microwaves. I leave out the tea as I know that reliable people like Mr Armada will insist I have a cup. Tea must be accepted when offered otherwise it's not likely to be offered next time (and I might be gasping next time). So whilst I enjoy a nice cup of tea or coffee, having one at lunchtime would be too much to hold in the afternoon. The morning's the most important time. It's imperative that my ten o'clock appointment makes me a cuppa otherwise I'm gasping by eleven o'clock. Can never ask for one, of course. If it's a new customer I just pray they 'do the right thing' and offer. Come the end of the day I can be swimming in tea, but I seldom refuse; it's part of the ritual. To old customers the 'tea ceremony' allows them to stop what they're doing, have a chat, find out about where I went for my holiday, what's the piano like at number 24 – you know, the Friends of the Earth people, they've got a sticker in the window and six bicycles. A sociological study might put the serving of tea down to the housewife's ploy to check that you're not stealing the family silver. Rather cynical! Maybe necessary where tradesmen are concerned, perhaps. Do sociologists consider piano tuners to be tradesmen or professionals, I wonder? Do you have to wear a suit and tie like Mr Burns to be a professional? No, tradesmen work with their hands. So I must be a tradesman (just like surgeons, then, who also use their hands – even use saws and hammers on occasion. But surely I wouldn't look right in a white coat?).

Thinking about this nearly made me late for Mr Armada the naval captain. Entering his bungalow in Walton-on-Thames, you almost think you're going to be piped aboard. His yachting cap is snug on its peg, pictures of ships and parts of boats adorn the walls. Mr Armada is a large, avuncular man dressed casually in a yachting sweater, navy blue slacks and plimsolls. He's got a great radio voice and is the sort who doesn't alter his voice or attitude for anyone. For example, it would never occur to him to have a telephone voice. So genuine, it would matter little if you were the queen or the newspaper boy, the retired sea captain is courteous to everyone and naturally interested in whoever happens to cross his threshold. Did I say sea captain or naval captain? Truth is, until a few years ago he'd spent thirty-odd years commuting into central London every day from his Surrey home. Mr Armada had had a humdrum sort of job in insurance. He just looked like a sea-going character to me, the sort you'd be happy to take orders from or wouldn't mind having on your side when there was a major swell and imminent storms. And, anyway, he was certainly a keen amateur yachtsman of some sort: loads of pictures of knots, books on boats; and he seemed to be away most weekends helping to crew.

But Mr Armada's second passion in life was music. So, as usual, we passed the snug on the left of the corridor and entered the living-room. It was only a bungalow but his grand piano had pride of place, filling three quarters of the room. It was a nice budoir grand (not big but better than those tiny baby grands which are little more than pretentious toys). After helping me clear the top he'd retreat and let me get started.

I always took my time with Mr A, made sure the tuning was firm because here was someone who could play. With time on his hands (and he'd been a long time without his wife, who'd tragically died when still quite a young woman), the old captain played just about every day, and wasn't afraid of a bit of fortissimo when it was required. Usually, the people who are not very good bore me to tears with their crude attempts at piano playing. With a forced smile I stand and watch with approval as they test the tuning, not knowing when to stop. Mr A, on the other hand, was modest and needed encouragement to continue. He looked so incongruous: a large, rotund man with a shiny head and chunky hands. Fingers thickened and calloused, no doubt, by many long weekends spent hauling ropes and doing running repairs to decks and sails. But to hear him play a haunting melody was breath-taking. Haydn, Mozart and Beethoven were his main repertoire. He epitomised the maxim: a good pianist can make a bad piano sound pretty marvellous, whilst a bad pianist can make a good piano sound mediocre.

Not that his piano was a bad one. You wouldn't believe that this large man, so laid-back and smooth, could produce such a delicate sound or run so nimbly up and down the keyboard: it looked physically impossible. But what I liked was when we got on to the heavier passages. He always liked to show me contrasts. I admired the way, although he wasn't a music teacher, he talked me through the pieces – "Here's a nice key change… what do you think of that? …and notice this tune in the left hand! There! Isn't Mozart clever: first the right hand has it and then, from another door, the left takes over." The contrasts, as I was saying, were very exciting. This is where Mr A let rip and the sound of the grand, no longer gentle, was on full throttle, with the lid up, charging the room with electricity. Big chords brewed up a storm, huge runs would smash into the walls, bounce off the mirror and rattle anything that wasn't tied down. From my view in a sunken armchair I was secure but always in two minds as to whether I should step in or not. For the grand was supported by three rather flimsy carved legs with 'ball and claw' feet.

Rather like Mr A's, the legs didn't seem substantial enough to support the colossal weight of (concerning the piano) thick, internal timber supports and a large cast-iron frame. Added to this was the silly piano stool upon which the great pianist was precariously perched. Having sat on the battered stool myself, I knew it wouldn't take much to be thrown off. Crescendo after crescendo, the pianist, deep in the centre of his own hurricane, full force being exerted now from the shoulders and back, the keys would be pushed almost through the key-bed. I was never sure what was more mesmerising, the heavy music screaming away or the body of the piano slowly beginning to sway: just like those buildings in earthquakes that can take so much swaying and then...

I was sure something would give. Either the vibrations would send the lid crashing down or the legs would snap like carrots. As an encore, there was always the strong possibility of Mr A finding himself flat on the floor with splintered matchwood all around. No doubt the trooper would have carried on from this position, no use of pedals but finishing the piece in fine style on his knees. Fortunately it never came to that, but it probably wouldn't have been possible to mention any concerns to the beaming Mr A anyway, as he would be bouncing on and off the stool, screwed-up eyes glued to the music flapping in the breeze of his unique physical performance. Whilst he would be delivering these thunderous blows on the cringing German grand, he wouldn't have heard my concerns. Part of me wanted the piece to go on; it was, indeed, very exciting, and I could never have brought myself to get up and actually tap him on the shoulder. That would have destroyed the whole performance. Worse still, it would have knocked on the head any chances of subsequent performances. No, thankfully the oscillating piano always gently stilled herself as the finale wound down. Mr A was never aware of the distant disasters that accompanied his impromptu impromptus. Climax over, he would mop his brow and come down to earth. "Gosh, I got quite carried away there. Mustn't keep you. Still haven't put your fee up?" He'd kept me back for at least half an hour, a half hour worth listening to. He was what my father would have called a very good amateur, which was high praise from my father, one-time student of the Royal College of Music in London.

I'd always allow an extra thirty minutes for this job; it was also inevitable that one or two notes would need another bit of attention after the performance. I think Mr A delighted in having someone who would actually sit and listen to him. He had two sons, but neither lived very close, and neither was particularly interested in the piano. He didn't have lessons and wasn't a 'performer'. He'd learnt at school and seemed to have acquired sufficient knowledge to learn new pieces under his own steam. He told me he'd gone to the local evening classes once. I suspect he was far more able than 'the nice old lady' who taught the motley group who came along for their ten-minute slots. He gave her a term and drifted back to his own regime.

It's amazing how undervalued the piano is as a therapeutic tool. Thousands use it as a source of private relaxation. I've had numerous customers say that they can't do anything else in the evening, returning from a day's work, until they've shut the door and played their piano for half an hour.

3.00pm, Mr Phelps

That just left enough time for a Mr Phelps, a new customer. Only three pianos today then, but that's probably near my average. Some days five (occasionally six), others three or four. I've never been like other piano tuners who race through the work ASAP and like them all neatly together, and won't venture out of a certain radius from home. It's good as far as time and money goes, but I don't mind cruising around a bit, visiting a part of London or a suburb I'm unfamiliar with (and my round just grew up in that haphazard fashion anyway).

That's not to say I haven't tried to stack appointments up neatly, reducing journey times and having a stress-free day. But that works out once in a blue moon. Caring customers are always prone to say, "Now... remember, next time you're in the area, just give me a call. I'll always fit in with you, dear, there's never any great rush to get it done, just do me when you're next in the area..." In reality, when you do ring up because you want to tie it in with Mrs Reynolds two streets away, who you're doing at 10.00am on Friday, the answer is invariably similar to what Mrs Green said after such an offer once: "Would you believe it! I can always do any time on Fridays but this Friday morning is the *only* time I can't do. Always have my perm on Thursdays but this week I opted for a Friday. It's at 11.15, daren't miss it this week because I'm going to a wedding on the Saturday and, anyway, Friday mornings are apparently half-price this month, and being so close to the weekend I would never get another appointment now if I cancelled, not at this time of year. Know what I mean, dear?"

"Not to worry, it was just a thought."

"Well, who is this lady who lives near me? Maybe we could swap, what's her name, do I know her?" It's easy to get into a bizarre situation of unknown-to-each-other customers ringing round, negotiating appointments. Unless they do actually know each other, of course, I have to do the ringing round and have more 'enjoyable' conversations that all too frequently land up going round in circles. "Hello. Turner here. No luck, I'm afraid. Mrs Reynolds needs the first appointment as she's going into town to have lunch with a friend."

"Is she the Mrs Reynolds from the bowls club?"

"No, I don't think so... The only time she could have done is the end of the day, about 4.30/5.00pm."

"Why didn't you say so, dear! Do me at 10.00 and this Mrs Raynolds or Reynolds at 5.00." Helpful Mrs Green sounded contented, as though she'd solved a conflict of nations. Having the two appointments so spread out now defeated the purpose of my call. Mrs Green hadn't seen this but, to avoid more conversations, I went for this arrangement: "Thank you for being so helpful, Mrs Green. I look forward to seeing you at 10.00 on Friday, goodbye. No, no, it's fine, it doesn't put me out one bit. No, no, there's no need to contact Mrs Reynolds, I'll do that. Yes, I'll definitely be finished by 11.00, you'll not miss your hair appointment. Excellent... lovely, I'm sure the wedding will be wonderful. Yes, indeed, well all the best. Good, Friday at 10.00, yes, goodbye... Yes, thank you... bye... bye."

It would be rather awkward doing Mrs Reynolds at 5.00 now as I'd planned to spend the afternoon in another area, but I'd need her as my fourth customer of the day. Maybe I could fit in another two who lived close to her. Picking the phone up to confirm 5.00pm with Mrs R, after dialling I waited and waited: she'd given up on my return call and gone out.

I seem to spend as much time on the phone as out on the road. 'Helpful' people such as Mrs Green always prove to be incredibly tedious rather than helpful. The sort that never stop to think that I might know the area quite well by now, that, in fact, for the past ten years I've used an A to Z almost on a weekly basis. In most cases, it's so much easier to look up a road name in an A to Z than listen to a waffling 'Guide to Torquay' approach: "Now, are you coming by bus, train or by foot?" (Perhaps she thought piano tuners are too poor to own cars.) "I'll be driving, actually." She sounded a little put out: "Oh, you don't have a dog then?" She thought I was blind but recovered swiftly, not waiting for an answer, "Driving? ...Oh, well, if you should decide to come by bus there's the 22 that stops by the park: they do allow dogs in there, by the way, and the 42, but that's only a single decker... Now, by car, you said?"

"Yes."

"From which direction will you be approaching?"

"Well, if you just give me the address I'm sure I can find it in the A to Z easy enough."

"Ah, you might say that but what A to Z do you have? We're just on the border, you see. I don't know if we're in *your* A to Z." I would have to give in and listen to a meandering description that eventually narrowed down from A roads to B roads, big roundabouts to little mini-roundabouts, to her road, to odd numbers on the left, to her side which were even numbers, to passing the peeling blue painted door of number 26 (she said no offence intended, but 'none of them work at 26'), to her house next to number 26, number 28, not number 24, the only one with a tree in the front garden, to her Cheshire cat that'll be sitting on the window ledge if the sun is out, to the brass knocker that has to be knocked twice for downstairs and once for the new lodger upstairs but only in term times. His name's Fred. He's a student (never seems to study but better than the last one).

My mind, in these situations, is screaming: "Just give me the address!" but I thank them kindly and wonder why I don't charge more to cover phone costs; and make out I've been scribbling their exact instructions down and try to call off. (Only once was I caught out when the caller said, just to be sure, "Now, read everything back. Let's make sure you've got everything down and haven't muddled anything up.")

Mr Phelps, my 3.00pm appointment, wasn't like that, thankfully. Well, I made out I knew the address (and in most cases I more or less do) and was able to look it up on the day. New customers always hold a little mystique. Will they look like they belong to the voice on the telephone? What condition will the piano be in? Most people seem to underplay the condition of their piano. A few do this because they're scared you won't come at all if they admit to not having had it tuned since the street party of 1945; or that, until a couple of weeks ago, it had been kept in a leaky shed at the end of the garden, but now that Amanda's turned eight and wants to learn... The others play down the condition of the piano because they don't want a stinging bill to put everything right. No, the cunning ones try to pass it off as 'just a regular tuning'. When you arrive, it turns out to be a day's work.

In Mr Phelp's case, he was quite specific: tuning was less of a problem; it was just a broken key, that's all. Could I bring another key? Well, I did. Most pianos have one of three different types of lock, so I brought the three possible keys. Trouble is: the terminology we use. I've since learnt that 'piano strings' are wires to many people, 'tuning pins' are pegs and hammers are keys. He meant there was a broken note (a hammer which I was able to fix); the lock or key was of no significance. I had asked him the usual questions over the phone, including the name/make of the piano (few customers seem to remember and so have to run and look), but the 'key' terminology had slipped me by. Turned out the piano was usually maintained by Mr Burns, but Phelps hadn't been able to get hold of him. I debated whether I should mention that Mr B had been awarded a contract for tuning celestial harps but knew I'd get the full "He was a dear old chap" eulogy. Still, he had to be told. Fortunately, Mr Phelps hadn't had Mr B's visits for as long as others in the area, so his eulogy was that much briefer. Although I hadn't ever met the famous Mr B, I could even fill Mr Phelps in on biographical details I'd picked up from other customers. Annoyingly, I almost found myself saying what a lovely chap he was.

It may seem that I was ageist in some way, but when you tend to hear the same stories from numerous customers, the great Mr B or whoever loses its appeal. This is even more so when you can tell by their work that, in a few instances (but not all), the dearly departed tuner wasn't very good. You can see the shoddy repair done with sticking tape, broken strings that have somehow been knotted together instead of replaced or that cigarette ash is covering the insides like a blanket of volcanic ash. As for the tuning, you can see they've spent years of only tuning the middle register: twenty minutes, a leisurely cup of tea, bit of patter and out. He looks the part; now the children have all grown up and left, she never uses it anyway, he's not going to worry because she's not going to worry. The fact that the top treble notes are a semitone flat and the bass is all over the place, is of no significance, he was 'a lovely man... we always had a cup of tea and a nice chat'. Such tuners know well the adage: you tune the customer, not the piano. There is an element of truth in this. I have occasionally come into new work because the customer has not been impressed with the last tuner. All too often, I have seen that my predecessor has done a perfectly good job. They have not been invited back simply because, in the customer's opinion, they were too keen to get out of the house (in reality they were efficient and punctual with all customers), were 'rude' (not talkative enough) or showed insufficient tact when describing (frequently correctly) the owner's pride and joy as being little more than a pile of junk – being best suited for a community project occurring on or close to November 5th.

Being, on occasions, a dirty job, and as some tuners prefer to go round on foot, casual clothes and trainers were the order of the day for a few of my colleagues. These tuners suffered the same fate as some teachers of the 1970s (once considered trendy or unprofessional, depending on one's perspective, due to their long hair, jeans and sandals), who didn't conform to a certain mould linked to concepts of respect, position and professionalism.

On a few occasions I have taken over from an elderly tuner who has moved out of the area or passed on, and I can see they have obviously kept the piano in A1 condition. By the time me, the replacement, has been found, the piano might be 'on the turn' but it is still very evident that it was well tuned. The extreme treble, alas, is the giveaway in just a few cases. Whilst tuners obviously have good hearing, in some older tuners it does fail as far as the highest sounds are concerned. It's quite tragic that the whole piano is excellently tuned but, after about the top C, the notes have either been abandoned altogether and so can nearly be a tone out when you play their lower octaves, or have been over-compensated for. The tuner knows he can't hear up there, and so tunes them sharper and sharper, and hopes for the best. Usually, he hasn't realised just how sharp he has tuned them (almost so the strings will break). It must be a bit of a nightmare tuning notes that you just can't hear – like painting a picture with the light getting dimmer and dimmer.

A few lucky ones seem to defy nature and experience virtually no loss of hearing whatsoever. Mr Weaver was like that. Still a young man myself, I'd recently started doing contract work for Harrods. This was the store that could supply anything to anyone, from an Antipodean anchovy to the almost unheard of horizontally striped three-legged zebra. So a piano-tuning service was a must, and they consequently had a modest list of 'contract tuners' (not contract killers) to handle customers in different towns and cities of the Empire. Because I lived in the same area as Mr Weaver, when he retired I was eventually given a lot of his work. He'd only lived two streets away but we'd never met (if I'd seen him out on the street I'd never have known who he was, although I often eyed people carrying briefcases or tool cases with curiosity and wonder). The 'He was a nice man' greeting was played out as usual but it didn't take long to see that he always did a thorough job. As far as the actual tuning goes, a competent tuner makes it so easy for whoever follows in his footsteps. Mr Weaver, like many other tuners, was conscientious. He tuned the piano to *his* satisfaction. He knew that many a customer wouldn't know if it was in tune or not, but he tuned it in case another tuner should ever have reason to visit the house and examine the piano. It was unlikely to happen but perhaps he adopted the 'Treat others as you would have them treat you' principle. If that was my piano at home, would I want it sounding like that?

Although unusual, there have been times when customers have rung in desperation. Their usual man is unwell or on holiday, a string's broken, it's Polly's piano exam next week, could I help them out? It's a nice time to be nosey, enquire how much Mr Soandso charges, how often does he visit? I can also see what sort of a job he does, making me pleasantly surprised or sometimes wince, wondering how on earth the owner could possibly tolerate a piano with a seemingly demented, out of tune-cum-ancient-barrel-organ sound. On the other hand, the reward comes from customers who are shown the light. Doing what is to me and many of my colleagues a normal service and tuning, customers hear their pianos as they've never heard them before. "It's like another piano. I don't know what you've done but it's as clear as a bell." It must be like someone who's never been shown how to drive their car in fourth gear: how much smoother, quieter, faster and efficient it is.

No, like the sportsman who fears losing more than he enjoys the winning, I don't want my work being looked down upon by other tuners. As I tune to my standards and to those of my equally competent colleagues, it is all the more galling to have customers pass judgement on my tuning when many of them don't really know what they're listening to or what they should be hearing. More often as not, those you'd like to try it, whose opinion you'd value, need much more coaxing than those who barely know one end of a piano from the other. I even had one isolated case where a customer looked with amazement and hint of disdain as I started to tune her piano: "You only rely on your ear? Nothing else?" It turned out the last 'tuner' had used an electronic device to tell him when each note was in tune; my not having any such technological gadgets presumably made me look rather amateur in her eyes (but take his gadget away and where would he be?).

One of the reasons why many of the customers enjoyed talking about their former tuners is because of the length of service the tuner had given. Customers frequently estimated their tuner to be 'at least in his seventies', which understandably quite impressed them. Additionally, of course, they had become one of the family (almost 'handed down'): tuning the piano when little Johnny hadn't yet taken his grade one, and now tuning it for not-so-little Johnny's eight-year-old daughter. The piano had moved but there was always continuity in 'our Mr Burns'. I suppose I could tolerate the Mr Bs more if I hadn't inherited pianos that were the victims of grotty workmanship. For example, I sometimes found pianos that had strings missing or had repairs done that practically amounted to butchery. Broaching the subject of urgent repairs needing to be done (because the whole thing was likely to go to pot very soon) could be a minefield. Often it was viewed as the newcomer trying to add to the bill: someone inventing trouble. It was often my 'luck', however, that the poor repairs of my predecessor would give out very soon after my taking over the work, and I was viewed as a bad omen. If I had used a bit of diplomacy and kept quiet about notes in danger of failing at any minute, chances are they would fail a few days or weeks after my visit, and I would get a hostile phone call along the lines of: you were only here a week ago… we never had this problem with Mr Burns… could always rely on him…

Nonetheless, after taking over from several elderly tuners over a few years, politeness had always decreed that I should cock an interested ear concerning the piano in question and its former carer (and customers were generally pleased, after all, that they had at least found a replacement). Although rarely having met these men, snapshots of their biographies began to have a small fascination. Where had they trained, did they drive (despite getting on or having poor sight, some cycled), did they have children? Were their sons in the trade? Some devoted customers were also adept at giving something away about the tuner's mannerisms or foibles, which inwardly pleased me: "Smoked like a chimney", "Couldn't give him tea in the morning, would only have coffee", "Would never come after 4.00 – wife wouldn't let him out after 4.00 in winter because of his poor sight... amazing how he got around, though", "Always late, so I knew 10.00am meant 10.30, or 1.00pm meant 1.30, you know...", "He didn't mind a drop of Scotch, I had to hide it after a while..."

It was nice to know these men were human. Just a pity I couldn't put faces to names. But upon hearing Mr Weaver's name I found it a tall order to believe that, "The dear old man was ninety." As I worked for Harrods too, I was able to get his address (customers often knew their piano tuner's phone number but not address). I felt I ought to go and visit him as he might like to give me some information regarding the customers I was taking over. Some people have theirs done twice a year, others like them done three times. It would help me not to contradict what Mr Weaver had suggested, but my real interest centred around trying to match the so-called ninety-year-old with the quality of the work I'd seen: no flat trebles; in all his pianos I'd seen so far they had been very well maintained. Here was someone I could learn from; perhaps I'd pick up a few tips during our discussion of his former clientele. It didn't seem worth writing a letter, and a phone call might have been as far as things went, resulting in no meeting and no face to the name. So I trudged down the road ten minutes from mine and knocked on his door. If he was retired, he was bound to be in at around 5.00. "Mr Weaver?" It turned out it was. He had a nice big, detached house. Pleasant enough inside but with slightly peeling paintwork and the giveaway furniture of the 1950s; net curtains no longer pristine white. It was the house of someone in their last decade of life. Respectful but a hint of dust no longer seen by a clouded eye. A garden with an infinitesimal hint of getting the upper hand. The comfy 1950s furniture would 'see him out'. Mr Weaver looked remarkably well for his age; this was definitely a home belonging to a seventy-year-old, it was winding down.

It turned out that the energetic Mr W was his son, who had little to do with the piano trade. It was fortunate I'd caught him in, as his father had reluctantly just retired to a rest home in East Grinstead (his wife had apparently passed on a year back) and John, the son, was visiting the house in order to clear and prepare it for the estate agents. His dad, indeed, had turned ninety and was fast approaching his ninety-first birthday. What a lovely idea it would be if I were to go and visit him.

And so, following an introductory letter from John, I arranged to go down by train to visit Mr Weaver senior. At ninety he was quite tall, well turned out, with a firm handshake. Very little in the way of stoops and shakes. One lens in his glasses seemed to be deliberately smoked over, but otherwise I could detect no loss of faculties. It seemed to me that, with the passing of his wife, and the large house long empty of children, Mr W had given up going it alone. Any thoughts of being the recipient of prized tools or having a share in the accumulated hard-to-get piano parts, however, were short-lived. It turned out that Mr W still did the occasional tuning that was within walking distance of the rest home: taking on new customers at ninety!

Despite the two-hour journey, that afternoon visit was a very short one. Mr W was polite, though a little cool. It wasn't said but I think he wondered why I wanted to meet him when we didn't know each other and he was, after all, retired now. He asked me what customers I'd already tuned from his list of clientele. We talked of Miss Smith or Jones, or the lady with the beastly Bechstein. It turned out that I would be wasting my time advising her to move it away from the radiator: Mr W had been saying that for years. In only fifteen minutes or so, pleasantries said, he prompted my departure: "Well, if you don't want another cup of tea, best be off. You don't want to be stuck in a place like this at your age." It was a pleasant enough place, and I had gleaned a nugget or two of advice but it seemed that would be it. After all, I wasn't family.

A day or two later it struck me how crass I'd been. From Mr W's point of view I was an upstart, probably a bit of a know-all, maybe had new-fangled ideas. And wasn't it a bit like rubbing his nose in it? Taking his customers, embarking upon a career he was having to give up. He was alone now: no car (admittedly sold years ago), no house, children in different parts of the country. The being in demand, the phone calls, Christmas cards from satisfied customers, had dwindled sharply. I'm sure he didn't particularly want to know about whoever it was that Harrods had decided to pass the work on to. I was pleased I'd met him, but how insensitive and guilty I felt.

It was a week later that I received a surprise letter. It was from Mr W, thanking me for my visit and inviting me to come down again. Best to wait until after the birthday celebrations were over in a few weeks' time, then I'd be welcome to come and spend an afternoon with him. This was a pleasant surprise. Maybe he saw me for what I was: green and slightly in awe of him. Perhaps, also, he could keep up a little bit with trade talk; and I could tell his customers that he may have turned ninety but he wasn't out yet.

Sadly, by the time I got round to arranging another visit, John Weaver had written to let me know that his father had passed away peacefully two weeks after his ninety-first birthday. There would be no more nuggets of wisdom, no more insights into what life was like for a young piano tuner in the 1930s and '40s. In his letter at least, Mr W had provided a glimpse of his early days as a Harrods tuner. Then, he covered a huge area which went right down to the West Country. It's hard to imagine him driving around in a sports car, but in his young days he was apparently an MG enthusiast and, as part of his job, undertook these 'tuning tours', covering different towns there and on the way back. He even had to go over to the gentry on St. Michael's Mount in Cornwall; case in hand, sea spray freshening his complexion as the boat danced its route across to the island.

John Weaver later told me that his father rarely spoke of his childhood. He'd apparently been brought up in an orphanage in Sheffield. Upon leaving school at fourteen he'd become a 'tailor's runner'. The close-work proved an ordeal, for his eyesight was not great, and so he was fortunate in being taken on by the London Aeolian Piano Company instead. It was here that he met a life-long friend, trainee piano tuner John Bullen. They were the same age, and qualified at the same time. A schoolboy-type bet had always been that Mr W would be tuning pianos for longer than Mr Bullen. They had originally meant that one of them was bound to eventually go into another line of business (or, being the thirties, one of them would be laid off). As the years turned into decades, however, with the two piano tuners now in different parts of the country, there was always friendly rivalry. Such things as Christmas phone calls would be deployed to surreptitiously elicit if the other was still working. It turned out that Mr W had always been quietly pleased that his piano-tuning friend had retired 'early' at eighty-eight. He had no intention of calling in the fifty-bob bet, of course.

1. Although the tuner, on his rounds, carries all manner of weird and wonderful tools, many of which would be unrecognisable to the layman, for a straightforward tuning he requires very few. He may also carry one or two concoctions in bottles, but unless he is like a few modern tuners who cannot tune properly without the backup of computerised gadgetry, he carries what he truly needs in his head, using his hands and ears to apply experience and skill. The photo above shows all that he really needs: a tuning fork, Papps wedge (with case) for muting strings in upright pianos, a rubber or felt wedge for grands, and a tuning lever ('tuning crank' being an older term, or in several other countries a 'tuning hammer'). Apart from the possibility of a screwdriver, quite often the able tuner only requires three tools, though always carries much more for the unexpected or occasional unusual or 'awkward' instrument.

INITIATION DELAYED

My own entry into the world of pianos was not necessarily because I dearly wanted to be a piano tuner. My father (with whom I didn't live until after I'd left foster care at sixteen) was a musician and composer. He taught the piano like many a frustrated musician and composer, to help finance his own musical interests, not because he got much pleasure out of teaching the piano to pupils who often comprised of children who didn't practise and adults who were painfully slow (and a few who couldn't understand why they hadn't been 'discovered' yet). Towards my last year at school (Barnwell Comprehensive) the careers teacher gave us one of those silly tests. You tick boxes, write statements and then the teacher uses a computer (his brain actually – the modern word 'computer' was gaining currency in schools but the actual thing was still a mythical machine) to work out what you'd most likely be suited for. 'Would you like to work indoors or out? In an office or with animals?' were the typical questions. The verdict for me, I think, was that I'd be most suitable mucking out cows: a farmhand. Maybe hands came into it; I wouldn't have minded being a chef or a car mechanic. Seeing the size of my father, I just knew that no amount of stretching or sports would ever gain me sufficient inches to be a policeman (not that I had sufficient exam results for this anyway). But my father had mentioned that pianos always need tuning; a piano tuning or repairing occupation was likely to hold good prospects. This flummoxed the careers teacher: how do you become a piano tuner? He would find out.

I was to go for an interview at the London College of Furniture in Commercial Road, east London. A strange name for a place that teaches piano tuning (as is another place that teaches blind people piano tuning, called the Normal College), but there you are. On the application form, struggling to justify why I should be given a place on the course, I'd mentioned my triumphant grade one piano exam and the profound statement that 'I would like to make pianos work properly otherwise people wouldn't be able to use them'. I remember a man showing me the insides of a piano and handing me a strange tool. "See if you can make this string sound in tune with this one." I didn't know then but I realised a few years later that I'd put the string nicely in tune and then got confused and put it out again. I put it sharp, that's no good, took it down again and then left it a little out of tune. The man then frowned, walked over and demonstrated (rather smugly) what he'd wanted. If he had said, "That's it!" after I had just put it in tune, or if he had given a demonstration first, I would have equipped myself much better. He also seemed quietly pleased in pointing out that on the application form I had just completed, under date of birth, I'd mistakenly put the current date.

The upshot of the interview was a letter several days later suggesting I stay on at school and do better in my woodwork and physics exams, then reapply. Having done rather poorly in all my exams, the school was not keen for me to stay on. I, in turn, wanted to get out and earn some money. So after leaving and going to live with my dad in London, I got a job working as a counter assistant in a camping shop in Buckingham Palace Road. London Town is not where I would have expected to find a camping shop but places like Victoria had several.

My younger sister later told me the story of Mr England, the science-come-careers teacher at my Stevenage school, who was now trying to follow up on pupils who had left. Had they got on to their chosen courses, were they in jobs they'd intended to do? Despite my sister trying to explain that, yes, he had gone for an interview for a piano tuning course but, no, he had not been accepted and was not pursuing that profession, so keen was Mr England to 'prove' the success of his department that he pretended (several times) not to hear my sister's explanation. She saw him glance down at his form and merely tick the appropriate box with proud aplomb, satisfied that the tick indicated a 'yes': Turner was doing very well in the piano industry.

Being a little slow, it was only after several months of working in the camping shop that the monotony began to sink in. It was a dreary 9 to 5.30 every day (and even Saturday mornings), and if a customer kept you after 5.30 you were expected to stay on. All this all year every year except two weeks' paid holiday. And the pay packet had been wonderful for the first few weeks; I was the richest man alive. It was *my* money, could do what I liked with it, until I eventually realised that there was little to spend and certainly none to save. By the time food, clothes, rent and travel in from south London had been taken care of, what was left? A pittance. The thought of being there until I was sixty-five was like a prison sentence. That's not to say that I didn't learn anything. If I was going to be stuck in the shop selling anoraks, tent pegs and sleeping bags all day, I may as well enjoy it. Selling became a great challenge to me. Trying to get a mum to buy a higher-grade sleeping bag for her boy's first Scout camp was tricky but rewarding. After a while, nine out of ten times I could sell almost anything to anyone. Rarely did a 'I'm just looking' customer leave without buying what they'd had in the back of their mind to buy later.

In the case of the mum purchasing a first sleeping bag for her son, that was relatively easy. "Don't buy cheap. Look at this one, see how it folds down so compact? Once that one over there is opened he'll never get it into his case again: far too bulky, complete waste of time. And for all that bulk it has so little warmth. No, as he increases his camping trips he won't thank you, you'll be back here again having to buy a proper one… Now this nice blue one I was showing you, yes, it is indeed twenty pounds more than the heavy inferior one, but your son won't be waking up freezing cold in this one. No, could use this on the Matterhorn in the future, he can't go wrong with this one, it'll see him alright for years… And now is the time to buy them, before they go up…"

The bulky one would probably have been fine as a first sleeping bag. I wasn't that expert on them. Just liked the names of the more expensive ones: Jungfrau, the Eiger Special; such specialist bags probably would have cooked boys if they'd been used on summer camps at Eastbourne. Still, having mastered the art of persuasion, boredom, after a few months, returned. Possibly because of looking rather baby-faced for my years, I was not given the responsibility of ordering new stock on a weekly basis (with my appalling school results, perhaps the manager pondered over my ability to read and write at all). Chris, a new lad, had arrived. Slightly older and, annoyingly, with 'qualifications', he was allowed to relieve the deputy manager of the tedious task of writing out the new orders (in longhand, in triplicate and with long order numbers). It was he who could stroll around with a clipboard, looking important as he perused the shelves and ordered what he liked. My heavy responsibilities were to serve, dust and make tea.

Chris was only two weeks into his role when I thought there'd been a mistake with deliveries. Box-loads of a rather dull camping handbook turned up. Normally we sold about two of these a month but, no, he'd ordered twenty-four boxes on purpose. Very confident, he gave me a 'learn from the master' lesson. "You see, it's all about psychology selling. If customers see lots of them out on display, there'll want to grab a copy. If there were only one or two on the shelf, they'd be suspicious: wouldn't touch them at all. That's why they haven't been selling recently." Over the next week or two I watched with eager anticipation. It was a great display, books piled high, couldn't miss them, but they stayed there. Occasionally, a customer would pick one up and flick through it with curiosity. Invariably, Chris's face would light up a few metres away, but just as he was about to sidle over and offer some encouragement, the customer, having seen Chris in the corner of their eye, would invariably place the book back in position with more alacrity than an escaping east London eel hearing the word 'jellied'.

Finally, not pleased at this new 'dead space' area, the manager had had to return most of the books to the warehouse. He took Chris off re-ordering for several months and had to write out the triplicate forms himself. I asked Chris what had happened to the psychology selling. He wasn't deflated: there wasn't anything wrong with the idea; it was only the month he'd got wrong. Wrong time of year for that sort of book; if only the manager had left them there a bit longer, the rush, apparently, was imminent.

At least he wasn't demoted to tea-boy, that was my lot. Until starting work, I'd had no idea just how much tea adults drank. I saw nothing in the beverage myself, but the first time I was asked to make tea for the staff I did it with great care. My aim was to please, and, despite the dingy bunker-basement conditions where the tea had to be made, I did my best: a nicely set out tray, all cups spotlessly clean, not being mean with the teabags, tea brewed for five minutes before pouring. I thought it was some type of test, little realising that, only two hours later,

I'd be sent to do the whole thing again. It was the two women staff who were the worst offenders. Not typical of camping staff, being in their late forties or early fifties, I now realise they would have been horribly addicted by this time. They were old hands at nattering and downing pints of tea. Occasionally the older one would have a nap after lunch in one of the small tents that was permanently on display in the basement showroom. Probably nothing better than nestling down on a down-filled sleeping bag that occupied the latest high-tech expedition tent. Even outside the tent there was a generally peaceful atmosphere as, for much of the time, the shop contained only one or two customers at a stretch. However, I noticed that some left with horrified expressions, after discovering the too life-like dummy with grey hair, slumbering behind the nylon entrance flap of the 'Tent of the Season.'

When I realised that the most important part of my job was going to be making the staff tea, I put plan B into action. I made it weak, 'forgot' that Jean took sugar, sometimes failed to boil the water properly: anything to put them off tea, but nothing worked. It didn't matter how badly I made it (even mixed the tea with coffee once), it seemed they'd drink anything. I was tempted to go round at 2.00pm with cups of sugared hot water but thought that was just a little too extreme. The manager, all credit to him, had said early on in a fatherly chat not to view the job as a long-term one. Inwardly I thought he was being incredibly disloyal to the company, but he was trying to explain that the company, through no great fault of its own, held little in the way of prospects for someone such as me. (Oddly, as he also lived in Stevenage, he'd even agreed for me to visit his home and be interviewed there rather than come up to London. The interview had been pretty informal, I remember him sending me away with some stamps – I'd been a collector as a boy and must have mentioned this fact.)

2. Rather before my time, when a home wasn't a real home without a piano. The 1919 advert had Cramer baby grands down at a snip: £148 guineas. By my time, the piano had been somewhat usurped by another, smaller, boxed instrument – the television – but I was to learn that the Harrods piano sale was still something of a highly popular fixture.

APPRENTICESHIP BEGINS

My dad had once worked in the music and piano showrooms at Harrods as a sort of 'between-jobs job.' It was he who suggested I try my luck in their piano restoration department. Unbeknown to either of us, it was the worst time to apply. The workshop, which employed about eight men, was virtually at a standstill. There were no suitable pianos coming through for them to recondition and put in the showroom. I went along and was interviewed by the buyer, who managed the showroom. He took me up to the workshop. It was full of strange smells; a glue pot was bubbling away and emitted the disgusting smell of (presumably) rotten horse bones. Carcasses littered the floor (piano carcasses, most of which were vaguely recognisable as pianos though appeared to be in various states of undress, rather like the buxom *Sun* models in the pictures on the walls that had been hastily but not entirely hidden with sellotaped pages from the less daring *Daily Mirror*). It all looked quite fascinating, even if it was incredibly dirty. The buyer introduced me to Ben, the workshop foreman. I can't remember what words were exchanged; it just seemed that, there and then, a job was going if I wanted one. I suspect the buyer had his doubts about my sticking with the workshop: I was still fresh-faced, of small build and perhaps came over as too sensitive. On the way out he added affably and genuinely: "If things don't work out for you up there, you can always come and try your hand in the showroom." Looking back, it's remarkable he took me on, considering I had no proper qualifications and no great aptitude for working with my hands.

It seems a blur now but that's where I found myself commuting everyday: to the Harrods workshop. Their slogan, 'Enter a different world', brought a wry smile to most of the employees' faces. I too entered a different world as I embarked on my career as an 'improver technician' – put another way – I was an action man of sorts. The playing mechanism (the hammers and associated parts that rest on the keyboard) are known as the piano's action, and I would be taught how to restore, restring, you name it, anything connected with the insides of a piano. Remarkably, as stated earlier, the workshop hardly had any work coming in at all for a while, so after hearing about my dad having recently purchased a cheap piano of First World War vintage that was already breaking down, Ben the manager suggested I bring in part of my dad's piano action and practise on that (Dad rather naively bought the old banger of a piano from a not-too-inspiring dealer called Spink's Second-hand Pianos in East Sheen).

Each day, to the curiosity of commuters, I would bring in remnants of what must have looked like a peculiar sort of bird cage or, to the more observant, the surviving bits of a piano rescued from a piano smashing contest. Ben, I suspect, was keen to show off his knowledge and liked to get his hands on piano actions the workshop didn't usually see. It was the sort of work he'd been brought up on (in north London rather than salubrious Knightsbridge), not the usual top-of-the-range Steinway or Bechstein grand that the workshop normally put into tip-top condition for the showroom. Here I was spending the first week or two being paid to work on the action of a piano belonging to my father (and all materials supplied free of charge)! I still have that piano today, it having done sterling service for my dad (mind you, it would be a few years before I could actually tune it. For that, we had to get someone in). I got one of the French polishers in the workshop to improve part of the woodwork and, showing his humour, he even attached a discreet Harrods transfer to the wooden key rail. These were normally affixed to all the pianos renovated or sold as new in the showroom. Possibly for some of dad's visitors to the rather humble flat, the piano from Harrods may have impressed.

3. This cheap, mass-produced upright actually served my dad well for many decades after it had been renovated. It was a straight-strung (or 'vertical-strung') overdamper model. The bass strings ran down top to bottom and so were not as long or tuneful as uprights which were overstrung (the strings run diagonally over the top of the middle section strings).

4. Above: part of the Harrods workshop as I knew it.

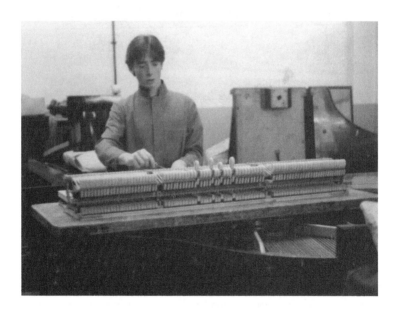

5. Tim Harvey, a fellow apprentice, regulating (adjusting) the action of a grand piano (for example, ensuring the hammers are level and that they repeat efficiently when played quickly).

The Harrods piano workshop was quite a contrast to the actual store. You got to it by passing the security desk at the staff entrance, and, as per their slogan, you entered a different world. For non-retail staff there was a whole new life 'below stairs'. Stockrooms, large walk-in cold rooms, packing areas, a few other workshops (jewellery, for example) and some staff restrooms were all situated in the huge basement area that was below the store and spread beneath the roads that surrounded Harrods. It also contained a warren of tunnels which allowed staff to get to the various underground departments, and the electric trolleys to whizz round and collect stock to take up to the store departments. Lifts, some new, others large and old-fashioned, for staff and goods, were operated by handicapped staff. I was told that some of the staff had worked there for years. I also put my foot in it by asking one of the operators about his boxing career. He looked a bit like a boxer – one hand was permanently poised ready to strike, but it contained a clawed fist; he also had a severe limp. In what turned out to be a joke in rather poor taste, I'd been told by someone in the workshop to ask him about his former boxing days, to which he angrily retorted, "Do you really think I could ever box with a hand like this?"

I found this unseen part of Harrods claustrophobic and depressing. Some of the staff had been conditioned to come in day after day, year in year out, staying down there all day, not seeing daylight until home-time. You could see it in their faces, the lack of expression or acknowledgement as you walked by. If a suited manager ventured down there (looking quite out of place), even the black, punch-drunk guy who worked in the post-room would shuffle along a bit quicker (he actually looked like Muhammad Ali's poor, forgotten brother). The zombies did have restrooms. These were not very inviting, being just stark box-rooms with cheap, none-too-comfortable furniture.

Most of the small nucleus of staff who worked in the

piano workshop had worked in traditional piano workshops outside of Harrods, nearly always around Camden and Kentish Town, which is where much of the industry was based – the area had once boasted around one hundred different piano manufacturers sending out thousands of pianos a year across the globe. By the 1970s very few of these firms were left but there still existed numerous piano restoration businesses. My older workshop colleagues didn't consider themselves to be part of Harrods as such or, at least, didn't view Harrods through rose-tinted spectacles. They would use the gas ring, normally used for heating the glue pot, to cook fry-ups for breakfast. Tea, too, would be brewed in the workshop rather than trudging off to the staff canteen. The problem with Harrods was that it was all very pompous and bureaucratic. Staff were controlled by an endless list of do's and don'ts. For example, a tea break was supposed to be fifteen minutes but it actually took eight or nine minutes to walk to the canteen (through long tunnels and passageways and then right at the top of the main building, then a long queue). Having reached the cashier it would have been time to turn round and run back. Management didn't like the straight-talking Jim Brown, workshop under-foreman, who rather looked down on the suited twits. They weren't prepared to make allowances, even when Jim had suggested having a longer morning break at the expense of losing the afternoon one. Situations such as this, and management's constant haggling over wages, encouraged Jim to lightly abuse the system from time to time (some years later, Jim would take over the management of the workshop).

Jim, although the under-foreman, also did some of the French polishing. His right-hand man on the French polishing side was Harry Smith, a stout Lambeth born and bred craftsman in his fifties (the local pub he still used was the Lambeth Walk – eponymous with a once well-known song). To get a massive grand piano's top shining with a mirror-like finish was a phenomenal skill indeed. It took months of preparation: disassembling, stripping, sanding, grain filling, repairing damaged veneer, staining, matching the various parts then 'bodying up'. This bodying up entailed applying coat after coat of polish via a wad of cotton wool wrapped in a piece of linen. Rub, rub in circles and figure of eights, sprinkling a drop of white oil from time to time, to lessen the friction. 'Look after the corners and the middle will take care of itself' was the useful adage given to apprentice polishers as they worked away on their panels of wood.

The shining parts that had been bodied up would then be left for a couple of months to 'sink'. The original bright finish would have begun to dull after being slowly absorbed by the grain. The piano and its parts would now need a long finishing-off session where the sunk and hardened polish would be worked up with more sweat and polish into a permanently hard, mirror-like finish. Half the skill was in getting rid of the oil. You needed oil to keep the 'rubber' moving, but if any trace of oil was left in at the end it would be more or less invisible for a month or so (the oil would add to the glossy finish but not for long). Eventually the oil would betray itself by its cloudy appearance, and customers would complain of a mysterious dulled finish and an oily residue which was impossible to remove completely. To avoid such complaints, the skilled polisher would have used less and less oil towards the end of his work and yet not had a rubber so dry that it dragged and caused streaks and other imperfections.

Such remarkable skills were slowly losing their importance as manufacturers of new pianos could get a gloss (or any other type of) finish by using polyester in a spray gun and booth. This process could be done in an incredibly short time and produced a more durable finish than a French polished piece (on the other hand, it was much harder to repair when damaged). That didn't bother Jim or Harry whilst I was there, and you certainly couldn't rely on a man in a spray booth to repair damaged woodwork or veneer. Try as I might, many a time I could see no hint of where the original damage had been after the polishers had repaired it. Their skills in making up colour and grain patterns with a pencil brush and a few lumps of coloured powder (such as brown umber) to mask damaged areas was an art form all of its own.

It was at this stage that I was able to pick up tips that would hold me in good stead when I later went on the road as a tuner (I grew to quite like the idea of being a piano tuner but didn't, at that time, see any obvious route towards that end – in the workshop I was learning how to repair pianos, not tune them). For a private customer, I once took a split leg off a grand to take home for repair. Having done a reasonable repair on it and matched the colour of the newly inserted piece of wood as best I could, I returned it. The piano had been temporarily propped up with a stool and books, so it was quite straightforward to screw/twist the leg back on. As they were interchangeable I couldn't resist swapping the repaired leg with the one at the back. Upon removing the supporting stool afterwards and inviting the customer to come in and inspect the 'repaired' leg at the front, looking from the right front leg to its neighbour on the left, she inspected it thoroughly and declared herself astonished at the standard of my work: they were identical, she just couldn't see any sign of the repair anywhere. The repaired leg, of course, was nestled away at the rear, where the room was darker and few customers thought to venture anyway.

Being something akin to an apprentice (Harrods weren't generous enough to set up a proper apprentice scheme linked to day release at a college), and as the newest member of the workforce, I frequently fell for the traps set by the other older men in the workshop. During the first few days some of the younger men would enjoy giving me a strange look whenever I picked up a tool to attempt a particular job. The look was an astonished 'what's he doing now/how does he think he can do that with that tool' sort of look. If I caught their eye they would quickly look away as though it was none of their business, though there was an inference of 'be it on your own head, sonny'. It had the desired effect of making me nervous to pick up anything. I was unsure about everything and wanted to ask questions, but of course wanted to show that I could be trusted to get on with things. After a while, one of the apprentices, Trev, revealed that they were only having a laugh. Occasional tricks followed, however, until the next new boy came along: "What's that, son, there in that bottle? Give it a sniff, see if it's meths, will you, I need some meths to clean these ivories." Keen as mustard, I grasped the bottle by its neck and shoved it straight under my nose, inhaling deeply in order to have the best shot at confirming the contents. Within seconds I nearly knocked myself out: eyes smarting profusely, I was told that I must have picked up the 'wrong' bottle, the one with ammonia in it. Similarly, anyone taking a week's holiday and not taking their tools home would find, upon their return, that picking them up would be problematic. Most of the tools would have been mysteriously dismantled or else glued and nailed to the workbench.

Wily Jim Brown knew how to make an easy fiver or tenner. I certainly wouldn't recommend this for one minute but he had a bet over some paint stripper. As part of the process of removing the old polish from a piano's woodwork (known as the case), the polishers slapped on plenty of chemical stripper. Rubber gloves were used, as if the stripper got on any part of your skin it stung quite badly (they should have used protective goggles too, but this was not in keeping with their macho persona at that time). Inevitably, even with gloves on, a spot of stripper would flick on to an exposed wrist or arm as the polisher scraped off the bubbling layers of old polish and set about rubbing the grain with coarse steel wool. Often, an improver (novice polisher) would be asked to do this, as it didn't involve a lot of skill and was also the dirtiest of jobs. The improvers had been brought up not to whinge if they were splashed by stripper: there wasn't much that could be done about it; it would just sting for a while. On the other hand, this unsavoury aspect of French polishing could be quite satisfying, as layers of history are removed from the wood's surface and the original grain can be detected underneath. Sometimes the piano was an ebonised one: when shiny black pianos were the rage or, alternatively, a mahogany piano badly damaged during the war was sometimes ebonised as this was a quick and efficient way of producing a smart finish on a piano where different parts didn't have to be painstakingly grained and matched (just make it black all over to hide the damage). When pianos such as these were stripped, it seemed almost sacrilegious to ebonise them when one could see the beauty of the original wood. Despite the trend or apparent bomb-blast damage, blacking walnut or mahogany pianos for fashion or economy didn't seem justifiable on any account.

Getting back to Jim Brown's bet, some of the younger ones had grown bolder, claiming they could dip one or even two of their fingers in a bucket of stripper for twenty seconds. When push came to shove, it was Tim who rose to the bigger challenge. Small bets were placed that Tim, an improver like me, couldn't last for up to a minute with his whole hand immersed in a bucket of stripper. Total madness, of course, all part of the arrogance of youth. With timer ready, he dipped his hand in nearly up to the wrist. Even my small experience had shown me that, for the first few seconds, the sensation is merely cool and pain-free. Nothing to worry about, the mind is told (and encouraged by the thought of extra money in the pocket). For ten to fifteen seconds Tim smiled and passed the time of day amicably as he no doubt pictured the pound he would collect from each observer very soon. The smile, however, soon disappeared and was replaced with Chinese torture-style contortions and muffled screams. The observers smiled broadly and reminded him that he was free to remove his hand at any time. I've often wondered what one of the suited managers (or customers who occasionally came to view work in progress) would have made of this 'procedure' had they walked in. They might have walked out impressed (or concerned?) at this handling of what they surmised to be a disciplinary matter.

Tim, meanwhile, despite the poisonous jellyfish sucking away at his decaying flesh, had his eyes, his watery eyes, glued on the timer and was counting down every interminable second. The clock, surely, must have stopped, there must be something wrong with it, it was going slow on purpose. "You can stop at any time," came the voices from the delighted elders.

They'd had their fun; now it looked as though he might actually pull it off: they would be proved wrong and, annoyingly, would have to cough up a pound. Perhaps he wasn't in as much agony as he made out, for, despite the twisted face and yelling, Tim kept his hand where it should be and wouldn't remove it until bang on the requisite minute was up. And he got his money, too, but I'm not sure if the enduring of blisters and lobster skin for two or so weeks after was worth the price.

He thought he was the kingpin, lasting a full minute whereas others had been playing with just twenty seconds or so. Jim Brown had seemed disinterested at Tim's feat, being no more than a very passive onlooker (he was dismissive of all us piano improvers. When he wanted one of us for a minute, he would yell out endearingly, "Oy, cod's 'ead, come over 'ere," rather than using our proper names – no doubt our proper names wouldn't be used for another ten years). Now, perhaps not to be outdone, he scoffed at the recent record and said he could do the same thing, in fact two hands, in a bucket of stripper for five minutes comfortably. There had to be a catch. He was accepting bets of £5.00 per person, however, and although we insisted it had to be a new, unopened tin of stripper (for maximum strength) and we would do the timing, Jim was adamant that, yeah, do what we like, two hands in a bucket of stripper was no big deal to him. It was tempting to spend £5.00 just to see the under-foreman squirm and prove him wrong; there was no way he would keep his hands in there for the full five minutes. We would get to see him in agony *and* get our money back!

Despite some of us surreptitiously checking his hands and arms for such things as barrier cream (we suspected there may have been a cream that offered some form of protection, possibly by neutralising the chemicals), all seemed to be above board. The tin, too, was brand new and therefore sealed. So after a good shake (to help activate the chemicals) and a generous amount poured into a bucket, within a few seconds Jim was standing there as though doing the washing-up at home. He seemed completely at ease, chatting away whilst his hands remained immersed in the stripper. The telephone went: "Don't worry, that can wait..." He seemed in no hurry to pull them out, and there was none of the customary screams associated with Tim's recent escapade or whenever anyone finds himself in the unfortunate position of having boiling water spilt on their hands. After five minutes Jim, at a leisurely pace, removed his hands and wandered over to the sink to wash the residue of stripper off. He did this as though he were about to stop for a tea break and wanted to give his hands a cursory wash. Casually, hands dry, he resumed whatever task he'd been occupied with before the bet, but not before collecting his takings from each of us. There seemed to be no visible ill effects. Whether or not his fifty years in the trade had lowered his sensitivity to pain or his skin had hardened with age, I'm not sure. We suspected the can of stripper had been tampered with in some way but all seemed in order at the time. On the other hand, he could have been experiencing excruciating pain but been a good actor and motivated by a healthy bonus for his next holiday. Something seemed amiss, but he didn't brag and we weren't going to spend too much time arguing with the under-foreman. It remained a mystery.

For my part, in the early days I tried to fit in as best I could. I discovered that when working on piano actions, everything normally has to be done eighty-five times (or eighty-eight if it's a piano with the fullest compass). If six different operations are needed to renovate one hammer/note (it takes something in the order of seven or more different moving parts to make one note work), then this has to be multiplied eighty-five or eighty-eight times. The work required a methodical approach. With so many individual working parts it was easy to jumble them up or lose some completely unless they were carefully numbered and stacked in the right order. Even before any repairs are undertaken, it would take a day just to strip down the piano, and at least another day to reassemble it again.

Although materials and parts were normally delivered to the workshop from trade suppliers, Trev had occasionally been sent out to get urgent things or to deliver small items that needed to be re-chromed. Heckscher of Camden Town (there since 1883) was the place for piano parts. Here they sold just about anything connected with pianos, though seeing them out of context made the parts seem all the more weird. Felt was sold in a variety of colours, shapes and thicknesses. You could buy massive sheets of the stuff to cut to your own requirements, or else buy such things as packets of felt washers that went between moving wooden parts to cut down on noise. The Heckscher family seemed to be comprised mainly of two brothers who couldn't have been more different in character. The younger one (in his late forties) buzzed around quite efficiently, but the older (and less slender) one was famous for his huge iron scissors which he used, in shaky hands, to cut strips of felt to order. He was a man of few words and his pace of serving was either slow or (in the afternoon or by Wednesday) very slow. Upon hearing the intercom he'd come creaking down the creaking staircase, resembling an ageing tailor in his three-piece suit. Often (he would say orfen) the jacket would be off and you'd just see a well-seasoned waistcoat and turned-up shirt sleeves. His saviour seemed to be his pipe. A suck on this and he could last a good five minutes on any activity. I was told that after seven years or so you'd even get a 'good morning' out of him. His brother, usually hidden away in the office upstairs, would occasionally come down and skirt round him, serving three or four drop-in customers to his brother's well-kept one per twenty minutes average. There was barely any eye contact between the two of them, and any interference on the younger brother's part would be given short shrift (especially when the famous scissors were in the elder's hands).

As the new boy it was my turn to undertake these outside errands from now on. Wishing to create a good impression, although quite new to London I didn't hang around. I followed the route described to me and, in fact, virtually jogged the parts of the journey not covered by tube or bus. The foreman was taken aback when I returned, mission accomplished, some forty minutes 'early'. Trev, perhaps wisely, had always taken his time. He would return, grumbling about delayed buses and nightmare delays on the tube, but having secretly enjoyed the best part of a morning off. Alas, having set a precedent, the foreman now expected all such errands to be done in a similar time. I wasn't really into metal-work but I'd made a rod for my own back. Trev, too, occasionally going in my place if I was not there, could no longer stroll down the road or pop into shops along the way. Still, we made a quid or two by claiming travel expenses. Bob

Eveleigh, the buyer and showroom manager, would sign a chit which we could take to the petty cash office for reimbursement. We didn't have to fiddle anything. Whatever we asked for he always put on a bit more, which we appreciated. I suppose it made us amenable when he wanted pianos moved around in the showroom from time to time. The suited salesmen invariably avoided moving the pianos by claiming diabetes or bad backs, though admittedly, if you don't know what you're doing, lifting/moving a grand piano can be hazardous (three men lifting and moving a grand piano correctly can make it look as though it were a light kitchen table gliding across the room). The more willing among the showroom staff were often a hindrance rather than a help.

Arthur, the hammer recoverer man, was another character I would be sent to visit. When a piano's hammers were too worn out – felt on the heads heavily indented from where they had struck the strings millions of times, worn thin and out of shape –

6. A modern view of Heckscher at 75 Bayham Street. At an earlier time, further down Bayham Street lived a young boy called Charles Dickens – destined to become quite a famous author...

7. A 1920s view of H. J. Fletcher in New North Road (they later became known and still trade today as Fletcher and Newman). They were another piano parts supply company we would use if Heckscher were out of stock of something. They were about the only other company of its type in the country. Based in the City, I never fully knew if there was any rivalry between the two companies. If I was in Heckscher and they were out of stock of something, it was rare but they were never backward in saying, "You could try our friends in the City."

I would be sent up to Kentish Town with a set for Arthur to strip and recover. It was either Kentish Town or Camden Town; Arthur moved around occasionally. This was because he'd managed to get the offer of a small backstreet workshop somewhere with cheaper rent (usually a corner of a piano restoration firm), or the tax man was on his heels. He was seventy-plus but couldn't afford to retire. Being a single man, he seemed to enjoy the work and being around people he'd known for years, or meeting fresh blood from time to time.

As a teenager in those times, I or Trev were not that particularly aware of the gay scene (though working at Harrods we became increasingly so). He didn't look like a typical gay man; he was old but had weathered quite well apart from a smoker's cough. It seemed a somewhat pitiful existence to be stuck in a small dank workshop, hacking up small blankets of pure white hammer felt to be glued and pressed on to German wooden hammerheads. As part of the war against biting cold during the winter months, an ancient gas oven would be constantly on. With its door dropped open, the oven seemed an incongruous item in the poky room strewn with piano wrecks. It was the only form of heating, however, and did little to counteract the numerous broken panes. Nonetheless, if a visitor arrived to deliver a set of worn heads, or perhaps collect a nice freshly recovered set, wrapped in brown paper, it was an excuse for Arthur to stop for a brew. The transistor would be turned off in deference to the visitor, and a broken armchair cleared of its debris. A slab of cheese from the 'fridge' (the damp outside windowsill) would be unwrapped with a degree of reverence, and the huge felt knife was temporarily deployed in cutting chunks of Red Leicester to go with the packet of TUC biscuits (nothing to do with the trade union; TUC was simply the name).

Although getting on, Arthur needed and still had wrists of iron. He needed them when cutting his blocks of glued hammerheads. The new felt was very hard and had been pressed into shape under great pressure. Rows of heads were glued to a sheet of felt at a time, and then, when dry, the presses were removed and the glued heads had to be separated into single heads again with a large knife. The complete process of recovering hammerheads was a hard and somewhat monotonous process, though requiring skill and knowledge which few in the trade had.

It was not that Arthur made a thing of being gay; me and Trev got better at sussing people out. We found him good company and liked to pick his brains about the trade in days gone past, or people we had in common. He was also knowledgeable about pianos as a whole, having worked for various piano firms over the years, but liked to talk about anything: in his younger days he used to own two Austin 1100s. He kept two so that there would always be at least one kept in road-going condition. His other idea, he said, was to buy a car carefully. Second-hand, of course; he couldn't afford a new one. But he aimed to buy a car so that it would give a year's use without any investment. No repairs or servicing; you paid a minimum price and, unless it could get through the next MOT without needing a repair, after a year you got rid of it and bought again. I think he'd tended to give up looking for cars around the time he'd stopped buying newspapers. One day Arthur had gone out to buy his usual newspaper only to find that none were available: they'd all gone on strike. So disgusted was he that he'd vowed never to buy a newspaper again because he'd been let down. And he never did, though I noticed he'd gladly take mine or anyone else's if they'd finished with it.

What I couldn't tell Arthur, during his life philosophy rambles, was that our under-foreman had confided that he'd once had a fight with him when they were young men. Arthur, even now, was a bit of a loud mouth (though I put that down as being partly due to him making the most of the few visitors who called on him rather than sending work through the post), and was also an enthusiastic advocate of the nude sun-bathing at (I think) Parliament Hill Fields. As apprentices, Jim Brown had taken exception to Arthur's friendly ribbing over a girl matter (like many of his generation, Arthur, at that time, was to all intents and purposes straight – few dared to come out in those days). To quieten him, fists were exchanged when Jim felt Arthur had gone on too long and too far, and Arthur landed up in a dustbin in the yard. That was Jim's memory of it, he insisted I make no mention of it to Arthur as it was 'all a long time ago'. Maybe Arthur would have recalled it differently, but the thought of these wrinkled men once again meeting nose to nose across a cobbled courtyard made me inclined to let sleeping dogs lie.

I had no idea that there was such a thing as a 'gay scene' until Trev, much more worldly-wise than I, enlightened me. The strange thing is that Trev was straight, girl-mad, a frequenter of Romford and Dagenham night clubs. For some reason, whilst walking around the store or in the canteen, he could pick out various members of retail staff and tell you not only that they were gay but what they were into. After much persuasion, he eventually got me to go to one of the big queer pubs of that time: The Boltons (the other being a close neighbour, The Coleherne), somewhere off the Brompton Road. He'd got a job there earning extra pin-money by serving in the evenings (and always came full of stories in the mornings); it only lasted a month or two, just to satisfy his fascination. I think he also liked the attention. It was certainly an eye-opener when he'd dragged me along for an early drink with him. The Boltons was full of men of varying builds and guises. Inside it was dark and crowded, there seemed to be certain sects, some in dark glasses and leather jackets, others in dungarees or sort of hot pants, frilly shirts and a 'Freddie Mercury' moustache. I didn't last long in there, too many beady eyes on me, though I could now see how Trev was such an expert at revealing the sexual tastes of some of Harrods' staff. The faces were all too familiar: boring George from haberdashery, Eric the china buyer (daytimes saw a preoccupation with china, but evenings were devoted to rubber). So ordinary during the day, I had no idea these men spent their evenings dressing up and groping other men. I didn't know where to put my face as some of them half recognised me and gave knowing nods. 'Come to bed eyes' I certainly didn't reveal.

Lee was the showroom tuner who used to come across to the workshop to tune the finished reconditioned instruments prior to their being transported over on a trolley. In fact, I was usually sent over to collect him, as he was blind. Lee, a likeable young man, was employed more or less full-time to keep the showroom pianos in tune. He could play and sing very well and so was rarely allowed to leave the workshop without giving us a number. I used to watch, intrigued, as he opened his trusty case and lightly fumbled for his tools. The tools, like most piano tools, were a peculiar mixture of strange implements that looked as though they were designed for removing foreign objects from foreign places in people from foreign lands. Nonetheless, in no time at all Lee would be making the now-familiar twangs as he ascended and descended the keyboard. He was very conscientious, his face etched with a serious look of concentration. Blind tuners are coached in speed when it comes to tuning pianos, and anything that held him up, for example a particular note that wouldn't rest comfortably in tune, would get him narked. The occasional obstinate instrument, if it was being really awkward, would even have him shouting and cursing at it in frustrated annoyance, which amused onlookers when this occurred in the showroom (though some took a double-take, not sure if he was actually cursing *them*).

I initially found it strange that I could stare at Lee and there'd be no look of recognition on his face. His eyes did not have the usual movement of a sighted person. I also found myself continuing with the acquired body language that helps the flow of everyday communication. Like we often do on the telephone, I nodded, smiled and used my hands even though the messages couldn't be picked up and interpreted in the conventional way. On the other hand, Lee often sensed when someone was there, just like other blind people who can detect sound shadows: different air pressure or reflected sound when passing a high wall, for example. I'd watch him intently as he worked his way through the piano and finished the job. At the end there would sometimes be false starts. He'd sit down to play and, after an opening bar or two, find he wasn't happy with a certain note. To us it all sounded fine. "What could he hear that we couldn't hear?" I wondered. No, he'd be up and making more adjustments before the playing could start again. I'd have my request list ready; whatever you named he could play it. The amount of verses he knew to songs was just as amazing. The more I thought about Lee's world the more I began to realise how memory was everything to him. When travelling around (and he only had a white stick, no dog), he had no visual clues. He had to remember how many stairs there were, what routes led off each corridor, how many stops it was on the tube until he reached his desired destination. I discovered that he'd more or less committed bus routes, train timetables and the Tube map to memory.

Things are taken for granted. The under-foreman wasn't one for explanations (there again, he'd come across blind tuners for most of his working life – he called Lee a 'butterfly tuner', because he didn't think he banged the keys hard enough). Jim would tire of people who wanted a detailed account of how to do something. In the workshop you mostly learnt by watching and picking things up, Jim wasn't a great one for 'bits of college paper and qualifications'. When he'd sent me over to the showroom to collect Lee, I think I'd just picked up from somewhere that he was blind. When I met him waiting by one of the pianos, there was an awkward silence after the enthusiastic first greeting. "Great. Let's go then," he'd said, and I waited for him to follow along. It was only when he appeared a little puzzled, still standing there, that I put two and two together and tentatively pulled at his arm and we started off together. Quite stocky and with a well-groomed beard, he didn't wear dark glasses and I half noticed that his eyes didn't seem to register things, but one never knows if blindness means total blindness (and even that concept is not as simple as it first sounds).

Like most other blind people, especially those who have been blind since birth or early childhood, Lee was adept at carefully educating the sighted. There is an irony here, as the disadvantaged in society have to work doubly hard to fit in with the more able. Grabbing someone's arm and pulling at it, albeit with enthusiasm and a genuine motive, is not a very nice sensation whether blind or sighted, though no doubt worse when it is unexpected and you can't see who the grabbing arm belongs to (but can hear a loud voice that illustrates to the local population that the 'poor, partially deaf-blind man' is being aided by a good Samaritan). The temptation for Lee and others is to rebuff the mugging-style 'You'll cross that road with me whether you like it or not' approach and make do on their own. He wouldn't want to alienate all potential offers of help, though, so skills involving assertiveness, tact and diplomacy are quickly learnt by the blind.

Lee, over time, showed me how best I could help him when he needed help. "Mind the steps," for example, is not that helpful if you don't mention whether the steps are ascending or descending. I also began to watch the reactions of members of the public when I noticed any blind person out and about with just their white stick. The response time for many was incredibly long; in the worst cases, some members of the public would almost glare back at the 'fool' who wouldn't get out of their way or had the audacity to nearly trip them up with their stupid stick. Of course, some people helped in a calm, sensitive way, but two stereotypes seemed to predominate. The first was our over-zealous 'grab first, ask questions later' model. The second was the shy or ignorant type who felt it best to leave well alone. When seeing a blind person standing at the edge of a pavement and waiting to cross the road (obviously not being able to see the sighted person), the onlooker either seemed totally unaware of the white stick and its implications, or they used their body language (pointlessly) to beckon/cajole the blind person across at the appropriate time, but were too timid to actually speak to the person concerned. They seemed to be stuck in no man's land, wanting to help but not knowing how best to give it (and were perhaps constrained by the notion that one must not invade another's privacy or personal space by getting too close). Very rarely, of course, an individual might have been put off by having had their past offers of help turned down in a rude manner; maybe others simply assumed that someone else would take control. Guide dogs are another issue I won't go into here, except for dispelling the myth that guide dogs observe traffic lights and know when they have right of way. They don't, but their remarkable skills would be less hampered if people remembered they are working animals trying to get themselves and their owners from A to B.

In the early days, when around Lee, I and Trev initially found it embarrassing to use words or phrases that we felt he might find insulting (part of my learning curve). Silly as it seems, in my conversation I tried to avoid any references to sight, such as 'I see' or 'Could you see your way clear to giving me a hand with...' Lee soon put us right on such issues. And he was fiercely independent. If there was no sign of someone to take him over to the workshop, he'd come over anyway, regardless of the whizzing trolleys. Out would come his collapsible white stick and off he'd set. The showroom itself was fairly straightforward. He was in there every day and there were carpeted routes that led to the other departments (the pianos being off the carpet and on wooden flooring). He'd give the china department a wide berth for obvious reasons but otherwise he'd tap, tap his way over. He was well known by most members of staff, some of whom liked others to know that they 'knew' the blind man. One or two of them, for some reason, would talk to him in a deliberately loud voice; maybe they thought he wasn't English or that he was deaf (insulting to a piano tuner!).

On one occasion when accompanying him through the showroom I overheard an innocent though strange remark from a customer. Once we had passed the lady in question, we were about to step into the lift as she remarked to her friend, "He's so lucky, isn't he, being blind. He must have wonderful hearing."

Us younger ones in the workshop hadn't come across a blind person before (or not close up, at least) and weren't that convinced that Lee was blind (I suppose it seemed a too cruel a card to have been dealt by the God of your persuasion). If he could play the piano so well and commute into work every day without a blind dog (we meant guide dog) then maybe he wasn't all that blind. I secretly thought that he probably got to Victoria station like everyone else and then, getting closer to Knightsbridge (which is where Harrods is), got out his white stick and commenced his role. It would have been an incredibly long and clever bluff to maintain for all that length of time. We just couldn't contemplate the thought of having to exist without sight. To us the notion was horrendous. We used to have discussions about what would be worse: being blind, deaf or maybe paralysed. Such discussions would have seemed a little bizarre had members from other departments overheard us as they walked along the corridor and passed the workshop. Hopefully, we were working while engaged in our deep, meaningful discussions, but hearing sentences out of context would have had even Jim perplexed: "Nah, I'd be deaf. No problem with that... Wouldn't have to put up with your noise, would I?"

"Can I be blind in one eye and settle for a paralysed limb?"

"No, blind is blind. You've got to be blind in both eyes... anyway, what limb would it be, leg or arm?"

"Arm! I'm not losing a leg. I can play football with an arm off but not without legs."

"I still say being deaf is best. You can play football *and* basketball… And if the music was really, really loud, maybe you could hear a bit anyway."

"Yeah, but I don't want to play basketball."

"You know what I mean."

"Yeah, well, you can't be listening to music even if it's turned up loud, that's cheating. You're either deaf or you're not deaf."

"Well, what about blind then? You didn't say if you meant completely blind, did you!"

"Of course I meant completely blind."

"What, when everything is totally black and dark?"

"Obviously."

"…But it wouldn't be black, would it?"

"What do you mean?"

"Well, if you can't see anything, you can't see colour."

"But black's not a colour."

"It's a kind of colour, I can see black easily."

"You know what I mean."

Over time, when Trev was certain that Lee, indeed, couldn't see, he wasn't afraid to have an occasional laugh at his expense. Young Bill worked in the workshop as an apprentice French polisher (old Harry gave him most of the stripping to do – thought he should spend the first seven years learning how to strip pianos). Bill was coloured (quite a polite term then; calling someone 'black' would have been viewed as rather outrageous or offensive), so Trev once tried to engage Lee in conversation about the 'immigrants' or 'nig nogs'. Bill and Trev were friends, but it was still surprising that he seemed to enjoy the game. Standing in a quiet corner of the workshop, after Lee had come over and was half-way through a tuning – with Bill not having uttered a word for twenty minutes or so, giving the impression that he was off that day – Trev would get on his political soapbox, with goading questions to Lee about Pakistanis and West

Indians. He half hoped Lee would get carried away in a National Front-type speech, with Bill then piping up from nowhere and pretending to be very angry. Perhaps fortunately, Lee was always diplomatic and would never have much to say on the subject. National Front politics were not to his liking anyway, but I think he had been given good advice as he grew up. I know I once asked him to lend me some money to tie me over until payday, which I later felt embarrassed about. Reluctantly (because we had become on good terms by then), he said 'no' because he never lent money to anyone. I thought about it after; from a blind person's perspective, trying to chase people you had lent money to might turn into quite a tricky business.

Sadly, another joke in very poor taste involved face-pulling. As most of the pianos were spread out around the room, and not pushed up against walls, it was easy enough to stand behind an upright piano, facing Lee whilst he was in front tuning it. Trev, with few principles at the time, would engage Lee in conversation. To all intents and purposes it looked and sounded as though a normal conversation was taking place, but while Lee was answering, Trev would be staring him close in the face and pulling the most grotesque faces imaginable. Sometimes Lee would be answering a technical detail Trev had deliberately posed for him to encourage a long answer. Despite the wild contortions (which included twisted mouth and a lizard tongue action), Lee was obviously clueless about such antics. Hopefully he didn't hear the juvenile sniggering in the background.

I'm ashamed to say that the no response from Trev's facial onslaught gave me more confidence to test our theory one stage further. I put it to Trev that if Lee was totally blind he wouldn't be able to see the flash that could be emitted from my camera. I should add here that Lee had been very tolerant and quite happy to answer questions about how long he'd been blind and whether or not he could see (he'd been blind since birth and could see nothing). Our 'interrogation' over several months about a personal affliction, once again, makes me realise how the unlucky fate of having been dealt a bad card is so much more than that. Not only do you have to carry your disability on a daily basis; you carry all the baggage that goes with it: explaining it to others, having people who see the disability rather than the person. In our youthful ignorance our questions had been quite blunt and tactless. On the other hand, we genuinely wanted to know if Lee had any concept of light and dark, or what colour is, and whether or not he could see in his dreams.

Getting back to the flash on my camera (my face is going crimson even now), uninhibited, Trev took up the challenge – after all, it was to be a scientific experiment. And if Lee could detect any glimmer of the powerful flash unit when it flashed, then we would be happy for him (though, strangely, it would confirm our suspicions that he was a fraud!).

The day loomed. The foreman and older men were out, probably inspecting pianos to see if they were suitable for restoration, and Lee had come over to do a tuning. The camera wasn't needed: all we had and required was the detached small hand-held flash unit that emitted quite a powerful flash at the press of a button. An argument carried out in sign language ensued, as neither of us now had the bottle to go through with the plan. Perhaps we could just come out and ask him, tell him it was only an experiment. But that would spoil the plan; he might be tempted to say he'd seen the flash when he hadn't. No, after a time, Trev decided to engage Lee in conversation and, whilst doing so, held the flash unit up to his face. I waited with bated breath, not knowing if Trev would actually press the button or not. It went off (silently) while Lee was in full flow answering a question about the reliability of the number 52 bus. It was daytime, but as the flash illuminated that area of the workshop, for a split second many thoughts seemed to cross my guilty mind: that flash was powerful; it could blind him... no, he was blind already... maybe the reverse would happen, perhaps it would kick-start his sight again... we'd be saviours. Or, maybe he would see the flash as only a tiny glimmer, a streak of light in his dark world: then he'd ask questions, find out that we'd been doing things in his presence but without his consent. Before these thoughts could be fully formulated, however, Lee was quick to exclaim, "What was that?" Trev and I looked at each other: he could see! It turned out he couldn't. As Trev had held the unit so close to his face, Lee had heard the minute whining noise the flash made every time it was activated, and he'd also felt at the same time a small release of heat straight after the flash had gone off. We had to casually explain that the flash had gone off by accident, mumbling something about the fact that one of us had been cleaning it, carefully omitting the fact that it had been held a few inches from Lee's face.

As I got used to the set-up at Harrods, it sank in how 'out of this world' it really was. It could be a strange and petty place. For example, there was a restroom for male staff, one for female staff and a mixed one (this sounds something akin to an exotic sauna set-up, but the restrooms were stark places with bare walls and cheap chairs). The buyers and managers even had a separate toilet and held their own key. It was a bit of a joke that there was a 'golden key', and that everyone strived to be promoted so they, too, could use the managerial toilets. I couldn't resist trying to catch a glimpse whenever I happened to be passing one of these toilets as someone was entering or leaving. Like other staff, I wondered what went on and what these toilets were actually like; maybe the toilet seats were gold-encrusted and there were jacuzzis and free massages for the hard-working managers. It seemed that was about all you could expect if you were promoted to manager: use of special toilets, although in the staff restaurant they also had special facilities. Laughable, really, the managers queued up and ate the same food as everyone else but had part of the huge restaurant sectioned off for them. The partition was a barely waist-high flimsy wooden fence, so everyone could see them, and if you were sitting in close proximity you could easily hold a conversation over the 'fence'.

The rest of the restaurant looked like a mass meeting of United Nations personnel, but it was quite cliquey. Different parts would be occupied by different nationalities: Italians jabbering away in one corner, hands flailing or prodding; a sari brigade would be 'next door' occupying a dozen tables and eating rice from Tupperware boxes; a few lone diners could be seen praying before raising food to their lips – they would be given a fairly wide berth by other behind-the-scenes workers letting the side down with their chips and rolled-up *Sun* newspapers.

With Harrods having seven floors and covering five acres of ground, Jim and Harry, of course, were not going to hike over to the staff restaurant every day ('restaurant' was an over-generous term, it was actually a humdrum canteen, though without the generous subsidy other employees of large companies enjoyed) so settled for bringing in their own sandwiches.

The workshop was right at the top of a part of Harrods that was separate to the store but could be reached by negotiating the huge basement area or by using a backstreet entrance controlled by more members of the Harrods security team. Being one of the highest locations within Harrods, in the summer months, against all the rules, Jim and some of the others would step up onto a workbench and climb through one of the large workshop windows in order to step out onto a tiny roof balcony hidden on the other side (you could almost reach out and change one or two of the thousands of coloured light bulbs that illuminated the store at night-time). Here they would enjoy forty minutes or so topping up their suntans ready for two weeks in Majorca. They were seemingly on top of the world, could see all the tops of the other key buildings; could even look down and glimpse the occasional occupant in their apartment. "Cor, look at that bird stripping off!" Jim would exclaim; the 'bird', preparing for a shower, was totally oblivious (or perhaps not) of those who held high office in the House of Fraser. It must have looked an odd sight, this rather wizened, knocking-on-seventy craftsman clambering through a window and stepping out on to part of the roof. With rough hands, faded tattoos, black fingernails and palms stained with walnut polish, there he snoozed clad only in his St. Christopher, socks and Y-fronts. Hard luck if the phone rang. Lunch break was lunch break!

For all of the employees, the pay and conditions at Harrods left a lot to be desired. Harry, the French polisher who worked alongside Jim, was a long-time resident of the Lambeth Walk. To a certain extent he was stuck in a time warp. He was always humming old hits from the thirties and forties, reminiscing about the war. Jim was dubious about Harry's time in Africa and elsewhere; his descriptions of the stench of rotting flesh or the sight of dead bodies were too graphic and hinted at being lifted from a book or film. When pushed, Harry could seldom give precise details about anything to do with location or date. Still, Jim concurred with Harry's cynical attitude towards the Harrods hierarchy. "The wages of sin are death and a curse," he would moan, finishing with, "but the wages of Harrods are a ******* sight worse."

Christmas time, when Harrods was working overtime to make a killing, would see a large room across the corridor from the workshop stockpiled with Harrods' special Christmas hampers, puddings and cakes. Several times a week you'd hear the footsteps along the corridor and a clunking of keys as the padlock was removed from the door. More supplies, we saw, were being taken down to the food hall. If two trips were needed on the same daily visit to the stockroom, it was noticed that the door was not always locked up between visits. One day, it was like a scene from *The Great Escape*. Nobody had mentioned anything of a plan to actually steal a Christmas cake (the hampers were too large to go for, and the puddings needed cooking), but many had been the day when Harry had sparked hunger pains by saying how well a slice of 'that' cake would go down with the afternoon tea (these yearnings were peppered with mention of the fact that, "We di'ent ge' no cake in the war, you know, never even saw a banana... saw a kid after the war who thought you ett the things wi' the skin still on.").

Harry's wishes eventually came true one day close to Christmas when pregnant Jim, put out about something the hierarchy had done, emerged seemingly from nowhere with a Christmas cake rather poorly hidden under his apron. Harry never went far if he could help it. For lunch he always sat on a big, old wooden chair with arm-rests that was all of a metre away from his workbench. It had a container underneath for sheet music, and looked rather like a commode built for a very large person. Eating his sandwiches whilst ensconced on this commode, his eyes bulged at what pregnant Jim revealed. The Christmas cake Jim had under his oily apron looked remarkably like the deluxe ones in the room opposite the corridor, the room that happened to have its door left ajar right now. "Consider it our Xmas bonus," he said, wiping a large felt-knife clean on his heavily stained apron (never cleaned, just thrown away about twice a year). In no time the tea was being stirred with a screwdriver, and napkins torn from sheets of upturned sandpaper added to the incongruous scene. Never mind the waft of turps or meths, the POWs sat huddled round the gas ring enjoying a cake fit for kings. They'd tried to destroy the packaging by burning it over the ring but the smoke had nearly set the fire alarm off; it would have been even worse if the water sprinklers had been set going and drenched them and the whole workshop in gallons of water. Instead the wrapper was thrown in the bin with a douching of chemical stripper.

It was a rich cake for rich people. In fact, it was almost too rich and not so nice in large quantities, but second slices were eagerly consumed as it was free (and some felt it prudent to leave as little evidence as possible). A consequence of this over-indulgence was the absence from work the next day of several of the workforce. Those who did turn up were noticed to be making full use of the staff toilets. In my case, wherever I happened to be in Harrods I felt every security man I passed could spot some crumbs that I'd failed to discard, and that I would be taken away for questioning at any moment.

There always seemed to be an element of Big Brother in Harrods. Tim, who had worked there longer than me, used to delight in pointing out the plain-clothed security staff to me as we were walking through the store on an errand. He seemed to know all their ways, telling me that whenever a regular VIP visited the store, it had been arranged that he or she would never use the same entrance on successive occasions (keep the assassinators guessing?).

It had been nice to have an occasional look around at lunchtimes, eyeing things we could never afford even with the (paltry) staff discount we were given. We were strongly encouraged by management not to walk the store, however, as we were staff and not customers. My faux pas might have been the fact that I had had the audacity to be seen eating an apple in the store one lunchtime, a manager practically pulled my teeth out as he wrenched it from my mouth, muttering something about 'decorum at all times!' The sad thing is, it was known that the buyers and managers weren't paid a particularly competitive salary or treated much better than anyone else. They were just the type of people who seemed to thrive on the rather suspect kudos of being an employee in the wonderful world of Harrods.

The store with royal warrants (later withdrawn under Al-Fayed's ownership) and forever of service to the stars, whilst frequented by famous faces and tourists, was actually many of the nearby residents' local shop. They were quite used to rubbing shoulders with someone they had seen on TV last night while walking through the often spectacular displays in the food hall – ice sculptures were a frequent eye-catching exhibit in the fishmonger section – but never mind the truffles and caviar further down; some were merely popping in for a loaf of bread. Meanwhile, some of the managers liked to think they could relate to their clientele, who might mention a well-known resort in the Alps. Though having never been there, knowing nods would be given by certain buyers as though it was a regular fixture in their own leisure-time calendar. They fooled few, however, as for many of them their employment at the famous shop was quite a come-down for what their families had intended for them. They should have been doctors and lawyers, but here they were working 'in trade'. Yes they wore suits and lapel badges of rank, but attempting to boss the plebs of the House of Fraser underclass was small recompense for not doing well enough academically.

After a while I could see that most of the plain-clothed security men stuck out like sore thumbs. The record department, though, was worth watching, as customers seldom clicked that the mirrored panels that separated it from the next walk-in department were two-way. When inside the record department, they couldn't see through the glass 'wall', but people milling around in the department on the other side could see them.

Jim Brown always laughed when he, like the rest of the staff, was searched coming in or going out of Harrods (through the staff entrance). He was amused because although they gave him a cursory search, they rarely, if ever, looked in his tool case. He carried it when called out to repair a newly delivered piano banged and chipped during removal. They just saw him as the old French polisher guy. His battered case stank of meths, but he boasted to us that his case contained enough chemicals and materials to make a couple of bombs (which was probably true).

Bombs were very much in the news then, with Harrods and other well-known establishments being prime targets for the IRA. Every morning, in fact, a ritual was played out before the store was opened to the public. At 8.30, over the tannoy system would come dated, though relatively relaxing, music. Wherever you were in Harrods you would hear this music begin mysteriously at 8.30 ('A Walk in the Black Forest' springs to mind). Then at about 8.50 an ominous voice-over relayed, yet again, the tedious message (seen and heard on buses and stations everywhere) about not leaving bags unattended or reporting suspicious items. The message was about 'all pulling together' for the good of the store, but it was not what one wanted to be reminded of every day: the place where you were stuck inside from 8 till 5 Monday to Friday (with nearest emergency exits ten minutes away) could go up at any moment. The rather pompous voice-over would be followed with another five minutes or so of sugary music (sending you to sleep rather than energising you for another day at the workbench).

It reminded me of my first day at Harrods. The only staff training day I was ever given still showed the inadequacies of institutional settings. This was nothing to do with the workshop – I soon found out that many Harrods staff weren't even aware there was a Harrods piano workshop (or other workshops, such as that of clocks and watches). Virtually all of the new intake on that day were destined to be sales assistants or department buyers. Dressed in their finery, as though it was their first day at school, they listened to the company spiel about market leaders, corporate image, service and duty. Everything done at Harrods, we were told, had to be the best; we were market leaders. Me, a green teenager, dressed in jeans and an open-necked shirt (no tie! shuddered the eyes of the majority as they edged themselves away from me) could see little point in this training. But the real message of the day, it seemed, centred around the risk of fire. Not so much risk to the employees – they were replaceable – but to the actual stock and fabric of the building. We were shown a graphic film of a fire that had ravaged a similar large store in another country. Fear was used to spread the message that we could all end up, so quickly, like pieces of blackened toast. We had a duty not to be careless ('careless talk costs lives', it almost sounded like). But by the end of the day, those who had drank of the company spirit were ready to start tomorrow with a clear vision: arriving on time, being physically presentable, wearing your staff badge with pride at all times, keeping stock replenished and dust-free, and knowing the fire drill.

Walking out the rear staff entrance each day, you could never be sure if you would be stopped or not. You should have been but if the security man couldn't be bothered to leave his seat or was otherwise engaged, he'd wave you on (with more seasoned workers it would be something like, "Fine, Jack. See you down the club later?"). One of the younger men in the workshop did manage to get out with a new double piano stool once. A nice teak one, very expensive. The stool was a display item that had been sent over from the showroom for a minor repair before it could be returned and (at some stage) sold as new. Having had the repair done, bold Maurice decided to walk it home. At the security entrance he boldly explained that, now that it was repaired (which he showed them although they didn't know what they were looking at), he'd been asked to return the stool post haste to the 'customer', who had been annoyed that it had got damaged during delivery. It's had a good home at Maurice Mansion ever since!

A culture of lack of loyalty grew up between some of the staff and those in power at Harrods, largely because they felt the famous store treated them poorly. I soon noticed that, socially, when I mentioned to people that I worked for Harrods, many were quite impressed and assumed that I was 'well looked after' – they thinking that its size and reputation for quality and expense would be paralleled in its staff benefiting from the huge profits made annually. In comparison with other stores and companies of a similar size, Harrods bordered on the mean. It didn't pay as well as its competitors. Unlike a well-known store down the road where the better the turnover, the bigger the annual staff bonus, Harrods didn't even pay a bonus at that time. Staff discount was also lower than in other large stores, and had limiting factors: you could only get it at certain (awkward) times, and not on all items. The staff social club, too, was a dismal affair and in no way compared to the nearby John Lewis Partnership, which had many clubs and even a hotel and water activities centre on Brownsea Island in Dorset.

Returning to the security staff for a moment, it may only have been a myth, perhaps it emanated from another store, but there was a well-known story that concerned a small group of Australian men, who always enjoyed an annual visit to the store each Christmas (I never discovered if they lived permanently in London or really were seasonal visitors). There could be nothing better than foraging for goods to take back to their families. Harrods was the place: presents for wives and the kids could easily be obtained in one major session. Note the omission of the word *purchased* and the use of *easily*. Having been successful in taking what they needed and finding it relatively easy to slip past the doormen happily opening the doors for them, they returned a second year for more presents from Santa (this time apparently ambitiously walking out with televisions and other larger commodities). It was only after the second or third year that the security staff could link the losses with this particular party. There would be no free Christmas next time!

However, in the last of their annual Christmas trips the Australian guys behaved in model fashion. Security were ready for them and had a discrete operation in place. No matter where the tourists went, they were watched on camera and followed at a distance on foot. There was no strange behaviour, though, and whilst the Australians may have dallied in choosing their items, they paid right up front for whatever they took. The security staff were both happy that the Australians had turned clean in the festive season, but just a little disappointed that they were not likely to be able to nab them for any criminality. Still, not to be fooled, they were vigilant in keeping a close eye on the visitors; all staff were involved in watching and following the party as they moved from one department to another. Fortunately, they shopped on just two floors and, laden with their paid-for goods, the uniformed security staff were only too happy to help them to the best exits, wishing them a happy Christmas.

Indeed it was a happy and bountiful Christmas, for whilst their husbands had been doing a little honest shopping on the third and fourth floors, the Australian wives (unwatched) had made their maiden tour of the ground floor and helped themselves to expensive jewellery, high-brand perfumes and some chocolates for the baby Ozzies waiting in the cars outside. One wonders if they took any Christmas cake for good measure.

I'd been an 'improver' at Harrods for a couple of years when Jim, for some reason, thought I'd be better off doing piano tuning. I'd fancied trying my hand at French polishing but soon realised my colour vision wasn't up to scratch after a salesman from the showroom came over to check on a matter with Jim. A front panel I'd been allowed to have a go at (making a small repair, then staining and polishing it) was drying nicely on my bench. The salesman, always keen to see if anything interesting would be coming over, asked to which piano the panel belonged. Peering a bit closer, he also asked, with genuine interest, about the small, strange orange streak that was just left of centre, calling it 'an unusual colour for mahogany'. I'd taken ages trying to match a filled-in hole to its rich mahogany surroundings, and had convinced myself that a closer colour match was nigh on impossible. I mumbled something about the panel not being finished yet. You don't realise how colourblind you are until people point things out. I remember later being a member of a badminton club. It was only after several weeks that an older man, sitting next to me while we waited for the next doubles game, asked me as tactfully as he could why I wore peach-coloured socks most weeks. It was only then that I realised they were quite an effeminate sight; although white was the norm, I'd presumed they were a fairly safe fawn colour and would never have worn them had I known they were of a peach colour.

Returning to the noble art of piano tuning, it was perhaps fortunate, then, that Jim had organised it with Les Garrad, a Harrods tuner who looked after the Northampton area, to come in once or twice a week to give me lessons (he still had a few select customers he'd kept on from his days when he lived and worked in London). Mr Garrad, as I called him initially, liked to don his suit and come down by train (on his senior citizen's ticket) to the big city. He would call in at the piano-tuning office on the fifth floor to have a chat with staff and put in his weekly claim. After that he would wander around the store; I think he liked to occasionally bump into one of his customers, perhaps proving that he was, in fact, 'someone' at Harrods, or maybe he wished to show that he too shopped at Harrods. He would eventually make his way up to the workshop in order to give me a lesson.

Les Garrad was a short, plumpish man. Given any excuse, most tuners will sit down to tune an upright piano (easier on the legs and back). Les, by force of his diminished stature, had little choice but to stand. With his distinctive bald head decorated with a skirt of short grey hair, he was vaguely reminiscent of a

Dickens character or could have been a long-lost cousin of the poet John Betjeman (though Les wore dark framed glasses). His claim to fame was that he had tuned the piano at Buckingham Palace (I got the impression it was just the once but I didn't like to ask the reason why). His second claim to fame, which I didn't really believe, was that he had once appeared in a well-known film with the actress Anne Bancroft. The film, he said, was called *The Pumpkin Eater*, but I'd never seen it (among her long list of films are the intriguing titles: *Gorilla at Large*, *Fatso* and *Dracula: Dead and Loving It*). No, I hadn't seen *The Pumpkin Eater*, not until many years later, that is, on the television. It was strange to see a young Mr Garrad – slightly plump even when a young man – bashing away on the same note, in the process of tuning an upright. He was in the film while Anne Bancroft could be seen wandering through various departments of Harrods in an anguished mood. I think the sound of the piano being tuned added to the melancholy atmosphere. Mr Garrad, closing the lid of the piano, turned towards the star and, without warning, gently... No, I exaggerate. No words were spoken. It was mainly his back view that appeared – for all of ten seconds. Anne Bancroft was in it for quite a lot longer.

Bashing away for ages on the same note was what one or two tuners I met later said they did when certain customers would stand and stare. Most times they were looking, of course, because they were fascinated, but, as I would learn later, some simply stood stock still and stared so hard it made you feel you were doing something wrong. No, keep playing the same note and hope they get bored!

With Les, back in the workshop, he would chat away, trying to disarm Jim, not fully realising that Jim considered him (and most tuners) a bit of a nuisance. On the one hand, Jim had encouraged him to come in and give me some tuition, yet, on the other, he wanted Garrad out as soon as possible.

Maybe there was an inherent disliking and suspicion of tuners. Contempt might be a better word. I know that he got the young Lee into a state when he was called over from the showroom to tune pianos that hadn't been fully restored. Depending on how much had been paid for them, or their age, some of the pianos had their strings cleaned up a bit rather than being completely restrung with a new set of gleaming strings. If a string is going to break then it will break, there's nothing that can be done about it, but Jim would make a big fuss and twist things around as though Lee was incompetent or had broken a string on purpose. What Jim was really concerned about was the extra cost involved and the time delay in getting the piano fully ready for the showroom. On hearing the bang as a string snapped, Jim seemed to take a small delight in complaining and blaming Lee: "What have you done now? Not another bloody one! I'm gonna take that out of your wages... there was nothing wrong with that string. You wanna be a bit ******* careful." It got to the stage where Lee (although he wouldn't admit it) was a nervous wreck when he was tuning an older piano. He knew it wasn't his fault; if he simply left a string that was flat and didn't pull it up, then someone would complain that it wasn't in tune. If it had to be pulled up there was a risk that it might break. There was no reasoning with Jim!

I later had more sympathy for Lee when I discovered what a horrible sensation it can be to have a long bass string suddenly snap without warning (remember, when you are tuning a piano you are almost in an intimate position with it, front panels have been removed and you are just inches from its 'bowels'). The problem is, some rusty strings look as though they won't take much adjusting without breaking, and yet they often defy nature and prove to be really flexible. Others that you think are perfectly okay can nearly give you a heart attack by breaking when you least expect it. With the bigger bass strings, the sudden bang of a breaking string is like a gun going off – even more unnerving when the string is only inches from your ear and eyes.

With Les, progress was slow. He liked to talk about pipe organs and church music. When we were working on the same piano, what he could hear I don't know. He talked of beats and intervals but I found it immensely complicated and mystifying. He seemed like a dolphin, not needing eyes to know what was in the box: sonar told him everything. Like Lee, there was another dimension to his hearing, and it was all so obvious and straightforward as far as he was concerned. For me, on the other hand, there was not only the skill of identifying the beats when tuning a string (the 'beats' are inaudible to most people but are what you need to be able to hear and calculate to tune strings accurately), but a host of other skills that go with it. The idea is to tune intervals on the piano so they emit the right frequency of beats for any given note and interval. The concomitant skills involved include being able to blot out other extraneous noise and harmonics, and also the art of manipulating the tuning lever (crank also called a hammer) so that it moves and sets the tuning pin just where you want it. By turning the tuning pin with the lever, the pin can be tightened or slackened (making the note sharp or flat, depending which way the pin is turned). Adjusting the pin so that it sets/rests firmly in position is much easier said than done, however.

Fortunately there were many old pianos to practise on, and Lee to quiz and observe too. Additionally, I was able to practise chipping up on newly strung pianos. Once learnt, chipping up is quite easy and rewarding. It involves using a plectrum to pluck the string while cranking it up with the other hand on the tuning lever. At this stage the piano barely looks like a piano, as all the keyboard and action have been removed (if it is an upright, it would have been laid on its back under the support of two trestles). Every single string, rusty and stiff, has been taken off and thrown away so that the piano carcass looks as though it has been disembowelled. With the strings out the way, the soundboard has been checked for splits, sanded down and re-varnished. Then the shiny new strings have been painstakingly put on. The system might sound quite straightforward but the old strings would have been measured before being thrown away to ensure exactly the right gauge of new wire is used. The strings on a piano not only get longer the lower/deeper the pitch is for each note, but they get thicker too. Each section of the keyboard has a different thickness of string (not easy to detect with the naked eye), and different makes of piano have their own unique stringing pattern. The bass notes in all pianos have to be sent away and hand-made. To make them heavier (so they can be tuned to emit a low note of the right quality and pitch) the steel wire is covered by a copper wrapping that has been spun round it by an expert string-maker.

Trev or I would be sent to Dettmers in Railey Mews, Kentish Town, to take or collect sets of bass strings. You could hear the string workshop from up the road, as the old-fashioned belts whirred away, driving the machines. The doorway to the workshop, which was tucked away neatly in a corner of a backwater mews, had the loudest siren going. With all the banging and crashing going on inside, a conventional door-bell would have been of little use. I used to ring the bell and wait for the siren to sound. Out of an upstairs window a strange little man would peer. With white hair and always with a fag end in the corner of his mouth, within seconds he would be at the door and beckoning you in. I found the appearance of this little man fascinating; no one had told me about this dwarf. He was always smiley, as though you were expected. His body was in average proportion, not with typical dwarf features, though he made me – rather short in stature – feel quite tall. He seemed to be a gopher, and was all the more remarkable for being able to get things done even though he was mute. At first, with the noise of the string-makers banging and crashing away, and the machinery stop-starting in bursts of energy, I'd shouted out my requests and he'd mumbled an answer which I thought I couldn't understand because of the noise. It was only when I once happened to call during a tea-break that I realised the dwarf man (I was never told his name) was lip-reading. He scurried off to get my order, smiling and, as always, using plenty of gestures. His grunts and pointing were accepted as quite normal by his workmates; I, too, found that the spoken word wasn't all that necessary. There was no question he couldn't answer, he'd show me the price on the invoice (strings were sold by weight), and if I enquired how long a particular set of strings would take, he'd remove his pencil from his ear and tick off the estimated date on a calendar.

The string-makers would rarely stop to hold a conversation, they had to get through so many sets a day. Their bread and butter was making sets of strings for the few English manufacturers still building new pianos. Firms that reconditioned pianos added a spice of variety (on some days some string makers might have said inconvenience). Sets for large, mature Steinway grands helped to relieve some of the monotony, and, with people calling in at various times, trade news and gossip could be snatched during fleeting intervals of quiet. "So-and-so has left that firm, started off on his own... Jack Rodgers have gone under... I knew Jack when he was just a tea-boy in his father's firm." The name Rogers was a familiar name to me, so it was sad to hear of another English piano maker going out of business.

News travelled fast, as there were only two string-making firms in the whole country, and each firm only employed about four men. It was pretty good money but hard work. It took years before any of them started wearing ear protectors. I fear one man, well known as a particularly skilful string-maker, started doing this too late. He began to be around less and less when I called in to have the odd broken bass string made to pattern (long after I'd been an improver). He was only in his forties but I was told he'd had to give up his craft due to tinnitus. The constant noise in his head, day and night, was causing depression and sickness. He was a craftsman sorely needed, as, by the time I was on the road, the other string-making firm had gone out of business.

There again, in the most recent of times, sufficient work for the remaining string-making firm has slumped as the rise in foreign-imported pianos and the increase in sales of electronic keyboards has hastened the decline in British manufacture of traditional pianos. When I last visited the string-makers I noticed that they were down to one (or two at the most) string-makers and were now sharing premises with south London piano makers, Welmar (who'd bought Dettmers out). I was reassured by the manager, however, that the night shift was now when the bulk of the work was done, particularly during the summer months. I bought it at the time, now I can see the real reason for the spurious response: no one wants rumours spread that they're having to lay off staff or that the business is struggling (there was no 'night shift').

Back to the chipping up. The new strings would have been cut to the correct length, put in place in the correct order and attached to the tuning pins. A technician in the workshop could do this restringing, taking a day or day and a half; or sometimes Jim would get a stringer in. The stringer would go round to various firms and do solely that: restringing pianos, doing the job in half a day. With the shiny strings in place but rather slack and not tuned to any recognisable pitch, they would need to be chipped up. With no dampers in, the strings would echo and vibrate even if you clapped your hands or shouted near the piano (it would have been ideal for mysterious or spooky film music). And so the magical process of pulling up the 230 or so strings to a very rough pitch order could begin. This chipping up had to be done as quickly as possible in order to get an even strain on the cast-iron frame. It would be the first of several chipping ups and tunings; the second chipping up would always immediately follow the first, as the strings were so elastic and needed much stretching (which is why new pianos are initially tuned about a tone sharp). Of course, had the action and keyboard been in place, anyone trying to play the piano would have heard a very honky-tonk sound indeed, but it was rewarding bringing a piano to life. Each tuning would slowly steer the piano towards a finer tuning, and the gaps between tunings could be left longer as it gained stability.

Whilst still working in the workshop for a couple of years, continuing with piano renovation, Jim had handed me more and more responsibility for rough tuning the workshop pianos. Lee would be ultimately responsible for fine tuning them once they had been wheeled over on the trolley. I could do a reasonable fine tuning but it would take me twice as long as Lee. The apprentice tuner has to build up pace and mental stamina. In the early days, after doing about two tunings, I would be mentally exhausted. If I'd continued to tune a third or fourth piano it would have shown in the lower quality of my work. Les and Lee, on the other hand, could do five or six pianos, all consistently good and with no loss in time per piano.

The main hindrance for Lee, when working in the showroom, was the noise factor. He didn't mind customers and salesmen trying out pianos, but it could become unbearable when people (some of them tourists) passing through felt a yearning to plonk on every keyboard as they made their way from the audio department, through pianos and, diminuendo, along the corridor to books (probably where an author was signing a copy of their latest book *How to Achieve Peace and Tranquility in the Modern World*). It was amazing how many people visiting or passing through the piano department didn't seem to realise that they were not the only person to have learnt Scott Joplin's 'The Entertainer'. It was played relentlessly by countless customers every hour, who presumably thought they were impressing others with their off-the-cuff performances.

I once saw a tiny young girl who was not yet up to 'The Entertainer' stage. Her foreign father, however, was quite oblivious to the fact that little 'Heidi', trailing behind him, was entertaining herself by smacking every keyboard she passed with the head of her baby doll. It was made of hard plastic, and she cleverly held it by its feet for maximum leverage. Smash, clunk! Pianos would almost cry out in pain as she lashed each one on her journey, chipping ivories here and there rather than the teeth in the baby doll's fixed smile. It was a delayed reaction, but a salesman tried to rush ahead and close the lid of each handcrafted gem, some costing close to the price of a new Knightsbridge apartment, but the five-year-old would instead try the nice pianos with their lids open on the other side of the carpeted gangway. "Honey, that's new!" the in-a-world-of-his-own dad eventually cried out, rescuing the damaged doll from his creative daughter. I'd like to say that that young girl is now a famous percussionist with the Berlin Philharmonic; she could be, or else a psychotic murderer who has corpses with smashed faces locked up in discarded pianos concealed in her squalid basement.

Lee would get peeved at people who came in to sit and play the pianos just because they were there, not because they had any intention of buying one. Some of them, like the Joplin performers, had an element of 'look at me' about them. Lee had perfect pitch (though, to kill another myth, this is not necessary for a piano tuner; most don't have perfect pitch) and would sometimes deviously play the same piece of music as the passing-through customer, only in a different key. Having transposed it a semitone, when played at the same time as theirs, the result was quite a clash and the customer would slink away wondering why their performance sounded so out of tune. This would give Lee a period of reasonable quiet before someone else's Joplin or 'Fur Elise' would signal the start of another series of performances from a new wave of passing 'look at me' clientele. When in a disciplined mood, Lee would clap his hands two times in a school-teacherly manner, hoping the temporary pianist would get the message and stop (if they were a genuine customer, chances are Lee would have heard the quiet conversation between the customer and a salesman).

Les Garrad liked to think he was the unspoken head tuner, often introducing himself as 'Garrad of Harrod' (some customers would unintentionally annoy Les by calling him Mr Garrard or, even worse, Mr Gerrard). Garrad was the sort Harrods would send out if there was a particular complaint or problem from a customer, but he also had many non-Harrods customers, including several well-known public schools in or near the county of Northamptonshire. On a couple of occasions I went up and stayed with him whilst helping to tune the many pianos that one particular school had. He was forever saying, "I don't know which way to turn," suggesting he was very busy. Most of the time he was, but I think he also inwardly liked being in demand, with the phone ringing at all times of the day and evening.

In his simple plain Skoda (of the old Czechoslovakian type) he would beetle along to places such as the public schools of Oundle and Rugby. "Doesn't use a drop of oil!" he would proclaim at intervals, obviously quite used to people expressing less than complimentary remarks about his – to put it kindly – very basic car. It was sort of frog green in colour, and he was forever adjusting the points (literally tuning the engine).

On my first visit, one winter, I remember his daily ritual began by putting the fan heater on an extension lead, taking it from the kitchen door to the car interior and leaving it on for ten minutes to defrost the windows. With such a small engine, the car was always freezing for the first thirty minutes or so. On journeys to the school the engine sounded as though it was working incredibly hard, you'd think you were racing along, and yet almost everything, from tractors to mopeds, would pass us by. Above the screaming rubber bands that must have comprised the engine and gearbox, Les Garrad would give a running commentary on customers as we passed their homes along the way. "You see the pub over there, the Black Bull? I rescued that piano. Was unusable, full of beer and cigarette ends. Spent two days on it... had to charge them forty pounds, landlord gave me forty-five... We'll pass the vicar's house in a minute. He's got a young family. It's an old Bechstein, always howling out of tune. His services are no good either. Not been here long. Likes the happy-clappy service, thinks it'll bring in more people. I try to steer clear of him in the town; have to go to St. Peter's now for a proper service... Lovely man, though... They have a choir at St. Peter's and a sung Eucharist. I know the organist well... he's got an old Broadwood at home which I tune. Always bang up to pitch, but you'd think he'd have something better, being a professional musician..."

We arrived at the school (quite a new one on his list, not the more well-known Oundle or Rugby public schools – so-called public schools that are not actually open to the public) and were not much warmer inside as it was half-term and the heating had been turned off. For some reason Les Garrad had very recently started tuning some of these pianos at the recommendation of a friend at the school (possibly hoping Garrad would do them at a cheaper rate than his predecessor, Mr Nibbs). I soon learnt that Garrad saw Mr Nibbs as his rival. "Let's check this one, bet it's howling out of tune," he'd say, with me in hot pursuit. Actually it sounded pretty good but I didn't want to contradict him in front of the head of music, who'd let us in. "Bet it's way down in pitch!" said Les, arriving at another one and reaching in his jacket pocket for his faithful tuning fork, giving it a knock on his heel and listening hard. He was trying to show me the shoddy work of this Mr Nibbs, but in this and practically every other piano I came across, there was little to suggest any poor workmanship. "Oh, he's managed to get *one* right, at least," Garrad would say, almost with disappointment, as we tried piano after piano.

He was a devout Christian, rarely missing Evensong, but he had his foibles. Still, we had to laugh when the head of music told us that one of the music teachers had come in to collect some post and noticed the piano tuners were in, and commented, "Oh, my piano sounds so much better now that it's been tuned." Knowing we hadn't started on any of the pianos yet, the head of music refrained from saying much, other than, "Oh, does it? That's good to hear."

Having to wade through some twenty pianos can be a daunting prospect. It's convenient and easier money because there's no travel time or expense, but there again earnings can be compromised because schools expect a 'bulk' discount. Also, school pianos often demand more time and effort as they get much more of a hammering than the average piano.

This school, in half-term was cold and eerily silent (and no doubt many of the pianos would quickly go out of tune soon after the heating was switched on again!). Garrad would fly through the pianos, forty-five minutes maximum on each one. It was a good survival technique: the best way to make the work pay and remain sane. Irritatingly, some pianos don't fall nicely in tune, some play tricks (occasionally the result of a design fault), and sections of it will go out of tune again soon after you move on to tune another section of the same piano, resulting in you having to retrace your steps and retune the offending section (sometimes only to find that now the next section has moved again). There are times when a tuner lands up having been through a piano twice, spending a couple of hours on what was supposed to be a routine fifty or sixty minutes tuning. But if good fortune is on your side, it will be a case of swings and roundabouts – one piano might need an hour and a half whilst another requires only twenty minutes or so. Les was good at not hearing the notes or sections that had gone flat again (or sharp sometimes). "It'll settle… I'll catch it next time… You still only on your second?" he'd say, going off in hot pursuit of his fifth one.

The school work was good in that you were left alone to get on with it, there was no noise or interruptions, but you rarely had a chance to stretch your legs or an opportunity to find a cup of tea before attempting to shorten the list. Still, I could see that this Mr Nibbs had done a good job: notes had been properly repaired, strings replaced where necessary and the tunings were very stable. You'd expect a piano to go out of tune after about six months, so it was all credit to him then that most of the pianos had hardly moved at all.

Although I didn't say anything, I couldn't understand why Garrad, usually so jovial and polite, nearly always spoke of Nibbs in a sneering sort of way. I guessed it was because he came from a village that wasn't all that far from Garrad's. He probably didn't want anyone encroaching on his patch. There again, Garrad spent much of his time tuning for his customers in Chelsea and Knightsbridge (he seemed to like being in the company of Sirs and the Hon or Lady Soandso). A little more gentle probing at a later date finally brought to light the likely cause of Garrad's poorly disguised hostility.

Several Christmases ago, Garrad, as usual, had tuned the grand piano in a nearby church hall ready for the annual concert. One evening a couple of days later, Mrs Roseberry-Fotheringay, rather perturbed, rang to ask of Garrad's health. He and Mrs Roseberry-Fotheringay (or Lady Rose Froth, as Garrad liked to call her when out of earshot) were old friends, Garrad had been tuning her walnut Steinway up at the big house for decades. She'd got it as a wedding present and Garrad, having been sent from Harrods, had been a part of the furniture ever since. Twenty minutes on the piano in the great hall, a sherry and a chin-wag, £20.00 in his pocket – if only every job was like this one, he'd often mused. Enquiries about his health, alas, had him puzzled until Mrs Rose-F explained that she'd noticed, while arranging the church hall flowers, that a new man was tuning the piano for the concert. She presumed that Mr G was under the weather and was ringing to see how he was (perhaps a polite way of checking to see if he was still alive).

It turned out that the newly appointed concert secretary, trying to be on the ball, had merely got 'her man' in to do the job, not realising that things had already been taken care of: Mr Garrad had found time to tune the piano, as he'd done for many years, and would invoice the committee in due course. He didn't say as much, but the thought of somebody else going over his work, of him being usurped (his annual appointment for the Christmas concert was as traditional as the village panto that followed it in January), was too much to bear. Still livid several years on, he explained that no sooner was the receiver put down by his informant than he was wrapping himself up and preparing to negotiate the lonely journey of the night. The right thing had to be done, despite a freezing car, black ice and unlit country lanes, he would check on the piano – the bleak mid-winter it may have been, but this was all in the name of service. Once there, a mad run round half the houses in the village eventually elicited a bunch of hall keys that the captain of the ladies' Thursday night B team badminton club was going to return to the vicar in the morning. Of course she knew Garrad, as he used to tune her mother's piano, so there was no hesitation in handing the keys over, even if it was a strange time to be tuning a piano.

Garrad let himself into the shadowy stone-cold hall. Here, no doubt conscientiously, Garrad, in his own words, 'went through the piano with a fine-tooth comb and left it in a fit state again' for the all-important concert. He went on: "I had to go right through the whole thing… can't leave a piano in that state for a concert." Feeling frozen but better in himself, Garrad returned the keys to the vicar's wife, who had no idea pianos needed so much tuning. Garrad, partly to do with his teeth chattering, couldn't quite explain himself to her as well as he wanted but emphasised there'd be no extra fee. He was praying – perhaps not the best choice of words – that her husband (the Rev Happy-Clappy) wouldn't come out and enquire of his recent desertion from their morning services.

I couldn't possibly comment to him, of course, but I could imagine him sitting there in that dank hall, being frosty for two reasons: feeling put out and pretending to put the piano in tune, and wishing he didn't have to be there in that dimly lit morgue of a hall. I've no doubt that the piano needed no attention whatsoever. Still, as one of the special guests, he would have sat there several days later quietly proud during the Christmas concert, knowing that it was his work enhancing the pleasant atmosphere as soloists and singers contributed to the festive evening. Not unless, of course, Mr Nibbs had been tipped off and was of a similar personality to Garrad. Maybe 'his Nibbs' had secretly gone back to retune the piano 'his way'. Was Garrad enjoying the fruits of his own labour, or was he unwittingly praising those of his rival? It's perhaps fortunate the two never actually met.

NOVICE TUNER

Having served my time as an improver at Harrods, and discovering that there was really very little increase in pay once I had moved on to supposedly fully qualified status, I had been thinking about what to do: should I stay on at Harrods in their piano workshop, should I see if they would take me on as an 'outside' tuner or should I go it alone somehow? My tuning skills had improved and I'd benefited from being sent out to do the occasional tuning or repair for the piano showroom. Even new pianos, from time to time, can have niggling faults (which we'll return to shortly).

Out of the blue, my hand was forced when it came to making decisions about my future. Ben the manager had already moved on, so Jim had been made foreman. Although a French polisher, he'd been in the trade for around forty years and was very knowledgeable. When he took over, perhaps they'd asked him to be much more careful with budgeting and costs. He introduced the idea of keeping a book for each piano that came into the workshop for renovation. How many man-hours spent on the piano depended on how much they'd paid for it in the first place and how much it could be sold for when in the showroom. Consequently, if the piano was cheap enough and of the right calibre, the workshop could afford to completely restring it and go to town on it in other ways (for example, revarnishing the soundboard and having the frame regilded). With other pianos, the time spent on it and the materials used required a much more frugal approach. We workers perhaps didn't appreciate it at the time, but possibly Jim was adopting the new time and motion method to protect our jobs, we were only aware that he was much stricter about not being late for work, nor did he ever allow anyone to go early. Even during the day, you were told how much time you had to do a certain task on a piano, be it refacing hammers or regulating the action.

Jim hadn't been there that long as foreman when he was obliged to pass the news on to us: by the end of the month the workshop would be closing. He was annoyed more for us than himself, as he was passed retiring age anyway. He'd also been a keen trade union member while working for previous firms. He was well aware that union talk (for those in the piano trade) was never taken seriously by Harrods, and it was clear that such things as redundancy money was not going to be paid. The state of limbo, then, while we workers worked out one more month, became rather bizarre. Because the workshop was closing, there were no more pianos coming into the workshop. I think Jim had almost given up and, feeling rather disgusted, didn't even come in every day. What were we to do? The phone seldom rang, London was in the middle of a heatwave. There never seemed to be any sign of management anywhere, nothing was ever given to us formally in writing, so on one blazing summer's day most of us decided to wander out and over to Hyde Park, which was only about five or ten minutes away (arriving early for work I'd sometimes see and hear the incongruous spectacle of Her Majesty's Household Cavalry from Knightsbridge Barracks trotting down the road, two abreast, heading for Hyde Park for a canter or two). After a bit of sun-bathing, a few of us took a rowing boat out on the Serpentine. There was just time to have an ice-cream before strolling back to the workshop before it was time to sign out. Believe it or not, those last few weeks were spent in that sort of fashion – carefree, either wandering over to Hyde Park or, on cooler days, sitting in the workshop playing cards. We'd have to come in every day just to say we were there, basically, but no one at Harrods was that bothered; perhaps both workers and management had resigned themselves to the fact that, very shortly, the workshop would be closed for ever. A few of the workers had already found new work before the last day, but for those who were still there, I think we all went over to the Bunch of Grapes at lunchtime for a farewell drink and that was it for the last day. Good luck, everyone.

After the Harrods employment came to an end, I found work quickly at a little Camden Town backstreet workshop (around Mandela Street, close to Heckscher, where I'd often visited to get new piano parts) which took in pianos occasionally for repairs, but mainly French polished new piano stools. They bought in these heavy rise and fall (adjustable) quality products direct from the manufacturers, which then had to be French polished in different finishes, depending what customers and piano stores wanted. It could be eggshell finish, satin finish or glossy. The owners quickly realised that I could do a really good job with the black ones, I could get a lovely 'see your face in it' shiny black finish, but my colour-blindness (which I had conveniently forgotten to mention) revealed itself when it came to trying to produce or finish off rosewood and mahogany effects on the other stools.

I don't know why I'd opted for a French polishing job; perhaps the money was good. It's true I was fascinated by wood and identifying different grains, but the piano stool workshop seemed to put me back into an almost Dickensian-like existence. No natural daylight came into the workshop, there was normally only one other man employed on this side, Fred, an old boy who was very helpful to me, but otherwise you had the daunting prospect of getting through piano stool after piano stool: sand it, seal/fill in the grain, colour it, leave for a day, polish it until it shone but don't leave any streaks… Talk about tedious and monotonous. The owner, not someone who knew much about the piano trade at all, would come in at random just to see if you were keeping up with your quota. I travelled home every day on my newly acquired Suzuki motorbike (it would have been more appropriate to have gone for a Yamaha, whose insignia on their bikes and pianos happens to be three interlocking tuning forks – Yamaha pianos was founded in 1900 by Torakusu Yamaha, the motorbike division of the company was established in the 1950s). It was probably fortunate I didn't use the tube, humming not perfectly pitched tunes, but of a full-bodied bouquet of methylated spirits and French polish. Added to this were filthy hands and fingernails that looked as though I had been playing with mud for most of the day. It didn't take long before deciding to review my situation (as Fagin might have said) to see if I could go it alone by making a living tuning pianos or repairing them.

Trouble-shooting is a skill that needs to be honed, as when a piano develops a fault it can be due to any number of things. An experienced tuner-technician soon has a mental list of possible causes and sets about checking these off in a systematic way. When you're new to the job, however, your approach is a little more hit-and-miss, and unless the fault is staring you in the face, a seemingly minor problem can take an inordinately long time to discover and put right. This was the case when I was sent by Harrods to cure a note that would only work intermittently; it was an urgent job and they couldn't find anyone else to do it at short notice. It would be my first chance to show them I was their man. Never fear, Turner is here!

It was a new grand that had been delivered to the plush Queen's Gate Hotel in Kensington; being brand new it was unlikely to be anything serious. The annoyance value of that particular note not working properly was apparently extreme to the guest pianist (it's always a note that would normally be judged as being rather insignificant that ends up as featuring heavily in the pianist's one and only party piece). The manager, it turned out, was new and wanted everything to be 'tip-top': the pianist must not be upset, and the hotel guests didn't deserve to have the ambience of the restaurant spoiled through the sluggishness of a B flat. More importantly, the booked pianist was Bobby Crush, no less!

The manager's eager expression slowly dimmed as the minutes ticked by (he wanted me out by 12 noon, when the hotel's restaurant opened). I'd had it in bits in minutes (which always looks impressive to the uninitiated), but now was prodding, staring and walking around the action and keyboard, which were resting not in the piano but on top of the closed lid. What I really didn't want was to have to go back to the buyer at Harrods and say I couldn't fix it. Firstly, I mightn't get out of the hotel in one piece, secondly, any similar offers of work in the future might be jeopardised. But this was no easy task.

It was bad enough with the cleaner practically hoovering up my trouser leg and asking me how long I was going to be, but I felt even more uneasy as the manager stood there, looking over my shoulder as though he were trying to find the fault before me. There seemed to be no broken or weak parts. The note, indeed, did work when played once, but failed if you wanted to repeat it in quick succession. The manager, now worried that the cause was serious, began to cover his back. Sipping his mineral water and tossing the occasional peanut into his mouth, he began pacing and thinking out loud: "We paid good money for this. We can't have this happening… I want an instrument that works! …It's supposed to be guaranteed, isn't it?"

Presumably, in his new role as manager he had thoughts of being a crushed grape when having to explain to that other kind of crush – Bobby – that the piano wasn't up to scratch. Fortunately, he was pulled away to speak to someone on the phone. I could relax a bit and think straight. It occurred to me that, although I couldn't see anything, a part may be fractionally loose (though I'd routinely tightened everything up) or something might be fouling the action somewhere. Heavy as it was, I grabbed the action and keyboard (which are screwed together as one cumbersome unit), slid it off the piano lid and stood it on its side, resting it on the plush carpet. With a gentle shake I could hear a minuscule rattle. A few moments later and out onto the carpet rolled half a salted peanut. With the action back into the piano in a flash, the note, to my delight, would repeat faster than a young Muhammad Ali on his punch-bag. Play it like a butterfly or a bee on a multiple stinging raid, curse had become cure in time for the manager to return and see everything together again. I demonstrated and then got him to try it for himself. "Wonderful! I knew you could do it. What was the problem?"

"A collapsed undercarriage which was aggravating an over-active butt-spring," I lied.

"Excellent. I thought it might be something like that… Won't you stop for lunch?"

Actually, it wasn't quite like that. I showed him the guilty peanut. He looked at me as though he thought I'd planted it there myself. With a further look of disgust, presumably due to my taking twenty minutes to find what was obviously to him a very simple fault, we departed with his finger wagging and the comment, "Don't expect us to pay, it's got a ten-year guarantee, you know."

Getting out and visiting different homes and establishments as a self-employed tuner appealed to me. Even on the few tentative tunings I'd done for Harrods while still employed by them I'd seen a variety of locations and customers (and slowly but surely I did get occasional work from Harrods – sometimes even a harpsichord or spinet). Pianos seem to crop up any and everywhere. I'd been in prison: walked along the same landings and corridors as the cons to get to the rehabilitation room. (The screws, though they searched me in a cursory manner, after hearing I was the piano tuner never bothered to look inside my case.) On other occasions I'd trod the boards of the Palladium and other well-known theatres whilst tuning for concerts or rehearsals.

One time, at the Victoria Palace, whilst there was no audience in the house, it was still enlightening to step onto the huge stage and look out at the vast array of empty seats. With no acting or dancing ability whatsoever, I still felt an urge to walk centre stage and make an announcement or tell a joke. I settled for having a good play after I'd put the piano in tune. There can be nothing better than enjoying the delights of a full-length (nine foot!) brand-new grand piano. The price would have been astronomical and could have paid for a couple of brand-new cars (though not so astronomical if one considers how many decades of pleasure and service such a piano provides), and in normal circumstances your average person – musician, even – would never get close to such a majestic instrument. It was quite a contrast to my dad's First World War Walter Crossley and Sons upright. This grand was a German, and in the trade we say that German pianos fall together. What French polishers and technicians mean by this is, when taking apart or assembling these instruments, there is no tugging, pushing or hammering necessary; every part just seems to drop into place smoothly and with the minimum of effort, they are so well crafted.

The power in the bass on this one was awesome: the longer strings gave it a beautiful and powerful resonance, making the whole piano sing out. There was a lovely lingering fade-away ('decay') when you kept notes and chords held down. On cheaper pianos the sound can be lost in only a few short seconds: a bark rather than a singing note. No, whilst working on this grand I was on the empty stage, tucked away near the wings, but I could look down at the empty orchestra pit or at the dimly lit auditorium. No one was around when I had finished so it was an opportunity to let rip and enjoy myself. Who knows, I thought, there could be a talent scout around, someone at last might appreciate my sensitive touch as I caressed the pure white ivories and slipped effortlessly into the haunting melody of 'Love Story'. The ivories were actually 'best grained celluloid' (as ivory is no longer used) and my opening bars of 'Love Story' were jerked to a halt by a voice over my shoulder: "You gonna be much longer, guvnor, only there's a re'earsal in 'ere at two."

Becoming a full-time piano tuner and technician meant I had to become 'official' and get an accountant. Mr Holdaway had been a little hard of hearing over the phone, and when we met in his office he was under the impression that I was a sanitary engineer. He did, however, put me on the right course for running a self-employed business. Just because I occasionally requested cash from customers, many handed it over with a nudge and a wink. I wanted cash because it was real money and saved having to go to the bank so frequently. People always seem to think that the self-employed are all on the fiddle. It seems to me that there is not much margin for not declaring everything you earn; the tax people won't have the wool pulled over their eyes.

And there I waited, by the phone, waiting for the work to come in. It was fortunate that I was still living with my dad, as there was not enough work to justify the title my friends gave me: 'The new pianoforte tuner extraordinaire'. Some advertising in the local newspaper and shop windows helped, along with small local piano firms recommending me to their new customers. There were numerous enquiries but not a flood of work. People would telephone at any hour of the day and give me a grilling over my fees (I suspected a few were the wives of other longer established tuners). Many of the more negative enquiries, which always seemed to occur as I was half-way through my evening meal, ran like this: "Yeah… erm … can I speak to the tooner, the guy ooh toons joannas? Oh, you sound a bit young to be a peeanna tooner, where d'you live, guvnor? …Would you travel to Bexley? Yeah, it's only dan the A2, can't miss it. 'Ow much do you charge, it don't need much attention, just a bit of tooning… 'OW MUCH! That's a bit steep, innit? And do you do repairs? What make? I'll go and see… I aint got me specs but I think it says Broadfoot… so you couldn't do it less for the first visit then? …And when can you git 'ere? No, that's no good, I'm only in Sa-urdees and Sundees… oh, could you do it t'morrer, it's Sundee t'morrer, innit?"

Wanting the work, I'd usually be pretty accommodating. This was for all manner of clients. I did last-minute tunings for concerts big and small, in marquees or the open air for weekend country shows and music festivals: rather bizarre being on the middle of a public common, surrounded by bails of straw, tuning a piano perched on a dodgy stage. Other locations eventually saw me tuning pianos in television studios, a piano beside the swimming pool in a luxury hotel – with residents splashing around just a few feet away – to wedding reception marquees or village churches. On one occasion, I found my work being videoed, though why someone should want a video of the little church piano being tuned for their daughter's wedding, is beyond me.

The Fishmongers' Hall doesn't suggest a particularly pleasant piano-tuning contract, but it was good regular work offered to me via Harrods. Situated on the City side of London Bridge, it was one of the various livery companies that populate the City of London (the Glaziers' Hall and Goldsmiths' Hall being other examples). It was an ancient and important institution, housed in an impressive building overlooking the Thames. The rather palatial main hall on the first floor was hired out for society wedding receptions, concerts and civic events. Whether it needed it or not, the grand piano was always booked to be tuned whenever there was a function (the cost of a tuning being of no significance to the thousands clients were being charged for the whole package). Often, whilst tuning the piano (if I'd tuned it a month ago this really meant only going through and checking it over), I would watch as the staff reached high with their feather dusters to brush off light dust on the huge portraits and elegant mirrors that hung on the walls that enclosed this enormous room; others, in white gloves, laid the tennis court-sized long chandelier-lit banquet table. Crystal glass, silver fish knives and spoons, all had to be within millimetres of each other and in the correct order.

8. Above: staircase in the Fishmongers' Hall; the earliest hall was built in 1310. I did tunings at some of the other livery halls also (for example at the Armourers and Brasiers, where the walls and staircases seemed to be littered with enormous shields, axes and hollow knights). I also tuned at the Baltic Exchange in St. Mary Axe. How fortunate I felt that my appointment didn't coincide with the terrible IRA bombing that destroyed the whole building.

I was on good nodding terms with most of the staff, but one chap always seemed to insist on waiting for my visit before he got out the hoover and began the task of hoovering the thick pile carpet, which seemed to stretch for miles. With such noise (a constant but not very musical C#), however, it is difficult to hear anything, making the tuning of a piano virtually impossible. Once, a polite request for him to let me finish first, had been met with a frosty, "You're not the only one who's got a job to do, mate... the hoovering's got to be done, and the people are arriving at four o'clock." It was a morning appointment. I think he really meant that he wanted to go to lunch, and also didn't like me, an outsider, telling him what to do (I had asked him politely). A mix between dirty and downcast looks had often been swapped between me and Charlie if I'd turned up at the 'wrong' time, the sight of my tool case registering equal disappointment to my spotting him emerging from the lift armed with his flexible plastic pipe and brushes, hoover trundling behind like an obedient gun dog.

He perhaps didn't realise that, in the back of my mind was the parking meter – so hard to find in the City – ticking away, devouring coin after coin. All the more, then, my embarrassment and inward annoyance after finishing a tuning and having to ask for his help when, fool that I was, I managed to drop my car keys as I entered the lift. It was of the kind seen in old movies, that somehow allowed room for small objects to fall through the wire gates and right down to the murky bottom of the lift shaft. The thought of my car stopped on a meter for a day, let alone my not being able to keep other appointments, was very worrying. But I also wanted to avoid at all costs telling Mr Montgomery, the manager, that I had somehow managed to throw my keys into the bottom of the lift shaft (remember I was quite young-looking and strived to give off the impression of an older and more experienced craftsman). Apart from my professional image being stained, he would have the inconvenience and expense of having to call out an emergency lift engineer (or would he just say that nothing could be done about it at the moment?).

My virtual not being on speaking terms with Charlie had, I think, been hastened through Mr Montgomery apparently putting him in his place a little after I had (tactfully) mentioned the fact that hoovers and piano tuning don't generally make a harmonious symphony. As there was no one else available at the time, rather shyly I told Charlie about my keys. He behaved much more efficiently than most managers would have done, saying, in an unsurprised and nice sort of way, "Hold on a few minutes and I'll see what I can do." Within minutes, he'd apparently turned the power off in the lift, acquired the relevant keys to the lift room, gone down into the basement and fished (a fitting term) my set of keys out. There was no gloating when he returned them matter-of-factly to their rightful owner, just a polite, "You'd probably be quicker using the stairs, the power is still off…" I don't know why, but my visits to the Fishmongers' Hall after that, always got a smile and 'Good morning' from Charlie. His hoover was never in sight. I think he liked the fact that he'd been able to help me; he didn't intend it, yet I always felt a little guilty in his company from then on.

There were the straightforward tunings too, but pianos could be kept in strange places: in cellars, garages or, one time, at the end of a huge bed in a tiny bedroom. The young woman who showed me in and left me to get on with it, failed to tell me that someone was asleep in the bed. I had felt a bit self-conscious entering the bedroom, which was full of personal effects, fluffy pillows, not to mention a large rosette over the headboard which said 'First Class' (couldn't work out why it was placed there). Rather than let my eyes glance around the room, I focused them only on the piano and set about the job in hand. Wedged between the end of the bed and the piano, about half-way through the tuning I needed to sit down for a moment and as there was no sign of a piano stool or chair, I sat on the edge of the bed to rummage in my case and get a certain tool I needed. I caught sight in the mirror hanging above the piano of a huge bearded man suddenly sitting bolt upright in the bed. Seconds later he bellowed in a heavy French accent, "Merde! Who you is?" and, after rubbing his eyes, seeming only slightly more docile than a grizzly bear, huffed like daddy bear, slid back under the duvet and closed his eyes and returned to heavy slumber. I very delicately continued to tune the piano as quickly as I could (rather more pianissimo now), then edged myself out of the room but keeping a mental note of where I kept my hammer. On coming down to get paid, the woman must have heard her partner's bellowing, for she half apologised, saying, "Sorry, Francoise works night shifts. He doesn't like pianos very much so I thought it best not to tell him about you…"

Other customers were odd but slightly more amenable. One had a delightful pianola grand piano in his house. It was from the 1930s and he'd paid to have it stained and French polished to give an art deco appearance, for he had almost a fetish for anything from this period. I think the actual house was Victorian, but from the moment you walked in, the front door, the lighting, mirrors and wallpaper were all in the art deco style. Even when he brought in a tray of tea and biscuits, we sat on furniture and drank from china all evidently in the very best art deco style (fortunately he didn't expect my fee to be at 1930s prices – 4/6 for an upright, 5/6 a grand).

As for the pianola, I don't think he could play it as a 'real' piano; he would just delight in putting on a roll of punched paper and demonstrate what the piano could do. Instead of pumping it rather frantically with your feet, as some owners have to do, his had an electric motor to drive the mechanism. As he explained, some of the rolls were actually made directly from recordings of famous pianists or composers now long dead. What you heard on his pianola, apparently, was how the piece of music sounded when Rachmaninov or Liszt had first sat at the piano and played it all those years ago.

Mr Adamson might have looked down on art deco, I don't know, but he was something of an art expert and worked for one of the famous London galleries. He had a large Steinway grand; its deep red rosewood case dominated one of the large rooms in his Knightsbridge basement apartment. The ageing though still quite slim and suave Mr Adamson could not play it, but it had been his mother's so he wanted to keep it (he played, instead, tennis once a week with Gerald in the residents' large private gardens). He also wanted to keep it as, according to him, the composer Rachmaninov had once played on it (which is quite possible). Unfortunately, its impressive size lent itself well to Mr Adamson using it as a display table for all his art pieces: cut glass, heavy bronze bowls, ceramics, pottery and many other peculiar items. It took an eternity to remove these and deposit them around the room so that, eventually, the lid could be opened, which was necessary for me to gain access to the tuning pins and strings. Mr Adamson, in cravat and flowery shirt, always managed to make me feel bad by dropping into the conversation how he was needed at the gallery, he'd had to take time off especially for me. He insisted I make these appointments, yet over the phone and in person he'd be huffing as though he seemed to begrudge having to be in for my visits. I think that is why he deliberately offered me coffee and, every time, reminded me that, "Oh, blast, terribly sorry, I've run out of milk." He knew full well I couldn't stomach black coffee. I think he was a terrible liar, probably never kept milk in the house at all.

At least he would help me a little with removing the items, but he would fuss so, giving the impression that many of the items were priceless (to me most appeared to be dusty bits of old pottery): "Ooh, do be careful... would you be so kind as not to place it so near the edge of the table... thank you so much... oh, I'd forgotten I had that sculpture, it's a lovely piece, don't you think? ...You will be careful, won't you? ...What, yes, you can put it there, I suppose... Will you be so kind as to put them back in exactly the same order after you've finished? ...Thank you so much... Now, how long are you going to be exactly?"

This same old routine was played out on every occasion. Putting them back was perhaps even worse, as Mr Adamson (something of a David Niven lookalike), being from the art world, had very precise ideas of how they should be displayed on his Steinway grand. He'd step forward or step back, seeing how the light fell, pushing a piece in a fraction or else turning it to face another way: "Don't you see? It can't possibly go next to the bunch of grapes." I couldn't tell him but my mind was focused on the parking meter, which was ticking away. The wardens were always very hot in Knightsbridge, and the cost of filling it (not to mention finding sufficient coins of the right sort) left small margin for profit; or profit would turn to loss if a ticket was earned. He would go on: "Oh no, not there, Mr Oliver, that would look grotesque, don't you see..." Apart from the fact that he couldn't play the piano, which didn't motivate me to try very hard on the tuning, and the fact that the piano seemed wasted – being one of his 'pieces' that only came to life when it had its six-monthly tuning – Mr Adamson annoyed me by insisting on calling me Mr Oliver, who was apparently my predecessor (poor Mr Oliver!).

It started at the intercom before I'd even gained entrance. "Yes, who is it?"

"Good morning, it's Mr Turner."

"Who?" he'd respond with a slightly annoyed tone. I hated shouting in the street to passers-by that I was the piano tuner, but stares aside, it had to be done.

"It's Mr Turner, the piano tuner."

"Oh, dear... is it nine o'clock already? You'd better come in." I'd hear the electronic buzzer release the heavy door lock, and enter into the lobby area. His apartment door was right at the back, down the dark staircase. He'd be fumbling on the other side of his door with his keys and attempting to release the various bolts, locks and chains. "Come in, Mr Turner, I hadn't forgotten you were coming."

As he invariably slipped back into 'Mr Oliver' over the early years of my tuning his piano, I can only imagine that he enjoyed reminding me that my name was of such minor significance that his brain had refused to store it in either its short or long-term memory. Alternatively, if I try hard not to be over-sensitive, perhaps he was simply a very busy man with a poor memory. On my first visit, after all, he had met me at the door, clutched my arm and led me in very carefully. "Now, there is just one large step in front of you. Be very careful. Do you want me to go first?" Nearing the piano, he gave what he thought were helpful hints: "Now, just behind you, I'd say about two steps, is the piano stool. It's a rise and fall one, so do adjust it if you want to." As I gently extricated myself from his grip and commentary, he seemed amazed at my mobility and independence. Being a sunny day, and my glasses being the sort that darken the brighter the sun gets, although he didn't want to mention the word, I think he thought I was one of those remarkable blind men who had chosen physiotherapy, basket work or piano tuning as a route to gaining their independence. I hadn't the heart to tell him that I could see, in fact could probably see better than he could, so put up with his over-enunciated directions and gentle pulling and pushing for several visits until he gained more confidence in my independence and amazing mobility. It might partly explain his eternal fussing over 'the pieces', though. And I did eventually cure him of greeting me on the telephone and in person as Mr

Oliver. When ringing to make an appointment, I started using the line, "Hello. It's Mr Oliver, the piano tuner," to which he was quick in correcting me: "No, I don't have Mr Oliver... erm, is that you, Mr Turner? Oh, dear, is it that time already? ...I'm very busy at the gallery, but when would you like to come?"

It was with some of my more local new customers that I learnt of such concepts as discretion and tact concerning their pianos (in the beginning: the hard way!). Often, many small high-street music firms turned over reconditioned pianos that were really old pianos bought dirt cheap, 'done up' (mainly for cosmetic reasons) and sold for a slim profit. I was often slow to cotton on that, with the free tuning given by the firm a few weeks after it had been delivered, my job was to go along and reassure the customer. Don't point out any defects, don't spend too long on it (or, alternatively, spend all morning on it but don't expect the firm to cough up more than the agreed minimal fee), just tell the customer what a bargain they had. The problem was I needed the work, so I didn't want a 'bad name' with some members of the trade (but nor, equally, did I want a bad name with customers). You could also make life very difficult for yourself, though, as, after pointing out a defect (or not glossing over a customer's query), the next few questions or statements would be: "How can we put it right, who's going to do it... They said it was guaranteed... Couldn't *you* put it right?"

For the price they'd paid, and for little Sandra, who could barely reach the pedals, the pianos were usually adequate. Some sounded like they'd been fished out of the Thames or that they were made from a cardboard box and rubber bands, but many customers would not have appreciated any difference in tone between theirs and one costing thousands (and both types would have had a smart, polished appearance).

Even when dealing with other customers who were the long-time owners of grotty instruments, I discerned – from the expressions on their faces – that I had unwittingly been insensitive. It may be that the said piano was a family heirloom, lovingly handed down to its present owner, a proud oldest daughter who ensured it was tuned once a year even though no one in the present family could play it. They'd eye lovingly the beautiful inlaid marquetry, original candlestick holders, and held the memories that went with the polished fixture. It had been the first major item Granddad had ever purchased. Despite blast damage, it'd been the life and soul of VE Day celebrations, having been wheeled out for that street party and many others.

In reality, what most people in the trade saw was a wreck, or a functioning antique that would work in a limited way if used very occasionally by sensitive fingers. The chances are, it had woodworm, was moth-ridden and with a wooden case whose finish was too dark and ancient for most people to have in their homes. Even if a trade buyer took it off the owner's hands for nothing, he could use it for little more than occasional spares. No, when tuning these 'delightful' instruments it's better to talk in terms of its character and history. The bass strings may have gone dead, you might not know how the treble really sounds because most of the notes don't work up there, but you can focus on the middle: "It's especially lovely in the middle, isn't it? …And the tone is not harsh like so many *modern* pianos today." The tone, in fact, is probably very woolly and disappointing, but perhaps the customer has grown accustomed to it. Speaking in these terms, you've more chance of going away as a 'lovely man' – someone who 'knows his stuff' – and being asked back next year (the new Mr Burns?).

There were customers who knew the truth or wanted the truth, and I became more adept at meeting customers' needs. I also learnt that you had to be careful what advice you gave. You could say something flippantly, perhaps because you were running late for the next appointment or because you just viewed the piano as yet another run-of-the-mill instrument. But any advice or passing comment would be picked up and thoroughly digested. You'd seen hundreds of customers since, and maybe a year had passed by, but you had to make sure you didn't contradict yourself as customers would remember, as though it were yesterday, the 'wisdom' you gave them on your last visit.

Even greater care was needed if you'd taken the job over from another (unknown to you) tuner. What advice had he given? Did he say it was on its last legs, did he call it a lovely specimen or did he play safe with neutrality, opting for: "It's an interesting upright, madam," or: "An unusual model, sir." Sometimes the piano would be a long way down in pitch. Had the last tuner left it down because it was impossible to bring up, or was he just lazy? Did it matter, should I inform the customer? Sometimes they were delighted after I had managed to raise the pitch of their piano (and once there it is easy to keep it at concert pitch if the piano is tuned regularly). Occasionally I had to 'go backwards' or undo my work when it was obvious (after breaking two or three strings!) that the piano couldn't take it: slipping tuning pins if not broken strings. If a string broke because it wouldn't come up (and then another one and another one), it was difficult to charge the customer for the extra repairs when I'd caused the damage through over-confidence (particularly if the other tuner had tuned it for twenty years without ever breaking a string). It was different if I had warned that the instrument was unlikely to stand having its pitch raised, but the customer had asked me to try.

On one occasion I advised a Polish customer not to have the piano right up against the radiator, something I have to say all the time. When I returned for its six-monthly tuning it was still in the same position. I was not surprised, as customers often ignore advice or, in this situation, are hard pushed to find an alternative place for the piano. After I'd finished tuning the piano I mentioned again (almost in passing) that it ought to be moved sometime (it was now winter and the radiator was blazing hot). It was a massive old upright and I didn't mean that I personally should get involved in moving it. But she hadn't quite forgotten and had had it in mind that she would ask me to help move it across the room next time I came. Her husband was back in Poland for a few weeks, so there was only me, her and her eleven-year-old son (who was the only one who actually played it).

Having finished the tuning, I had been looking forward to going home and didn't really want to be delayed nor be struggling with this monster which had no wheels and was sunk into a deep pile carpet. "Just across the room, that's all. I hadn't forgotten. I remember you telling me last time that the radiator would damage the piano permanently. Now you've just tuned it I don't want it to go out of tune, otherwise all your good work will have been wasted." I was a little surprised but pleased that the rather sensible son, a somewhat shy and skinny boy, was siding with me and doing all he could to discourage his mum from trying to pull it away from the wall. He backed me up when I said that it might be too much to handle; perhaps it could be done another time. He was gently scolded and, as it looked as though she was going to do all in her (limited) power to wrench out the toppling piano any way she possibly could, I couldn't let her husband return to see his good wife entombed in a toppled piano sunk deep into the living room floor.

It was only then, with the piano having been pulled right out from the wall, that the mother saw the evidence. There were numerous flimsy plastic bags strewn in what had been positions under and behind the piano. I wasn't sure what they were, but the mum eyed them suspiciously and didn't really need to open them. The boy Marek had disappeared upstairs. The little parcels were several months' supply of daily sandwiches for school which, presumably, Marek didn't fancy. The Polish explosion that saw Marek yanked downstairs, tears about to burst through, was followed a few minutes later by the mother recovering and drawing him to her bosom, wondering out loud how little Marek could still be alive after going for months without nourishment. My advice suddenly took on a new light; I had practically saved her son's life. But it was all part of the job; she thanked me profusely and I left with a sore back (and no tip).

I continued to get the occasional Harrods tuning to do but I was not officially on their books just then, so the work given to me amounted to about one a month to start with (such as Mr Adamson). They were mostly urgent jobs, perhaps when one of their tuners had fallen ill. On any job I did, Harrods and non-Harrods, I tried to do the best I could, as I wanted to be called back next time it needed attention. Sometimes, at the end of a job there'd be a look of horror on the customer's face when I told them how much the fee was (non-Harrods customers, that is). Oh no, I used to think, surely my prices can't be that much out, what do I do if she starts haggling over the price? Do I haggle, do I have a strop and put it all out of tune again and walk out? It was nearly always a relief, however, as most customers couldn't understand why I was charging so little (it was even nicer when a few rounded my fee up).

Trying to be thorough and helpful, alas, wasn't always appreciated. Two examples stand out. In the first, after I'd done the tuning for a small Indian lady, I noticed that the pedals hardly worked at all. They could not be pushed down very far, so they had either seized up or something was blocking them. I soon found out the cause. Some crumpled up newspaper had got jammed in the gaps underneath the pedals (possibly the grandchildren?). After I'd finished, inwardly pleased with myself I showed the lady the cause of the problem and demonstrated how freely they now worked. She wasn't that impressed, and explained that she never used the pedals and had put the crumpled newspaper there to keep the mice out. I was paid and thanked for the visit, but as I left the house she was already crumpling up new bits of *The Guardian* to wedge under the pedals.

To me, and I'm sure most pianists, the pedals are an important part of the piano, perhaps like the difference between a car with synchromesh gears and one without. Unless you're a Bach freak, the piano is not much fun without a sustaining pedal (you can take or leave the soft pedal!). From one visit to the next, the pedals will invariably need some adjustment and servicing. I tended to put the pedals right as an automatic chore as I wouldn't like to play a piano of my own with poor or non-functioning pedals (the usual and biggest nuisance being a squeaky or noisy pedal). I also included it as part of my service fee as it would help to keep the customer happy. Other tuners (and this depends on one's opinion, but some would say these tuners had more business sense) would do a standard tuning that was a set price and did not include any extras (because, to them, fault finding and/or doing repairs was a separate job). This could be a wise move, as I began to find out. Along with my customers who asked me to have a 'quick look' at the noisy pedal or dodgy note, I often found such basic requests could turn out to be quite a palaver.

Rectifying apparently simple pedal problems can sometimes involve getting on your hands and knees, crawling in or under the piano (dark and dusty) then sometimes messing about with screws and nuts that haven't seen daylight for years. For the unlucky tuner, one problem can lead to another as you find yourself taking piece after piece to bits in an attempt to get to the root cause of the problem. More often than not a previous tuner has managed to ignore the problem or has opted to throw some talcum powder in the works, to keep noises temporarily at bay. When it is your turn you find all tricks of the trade have come to an end, and you have to strip it down, and land up repairing various bits as you head towards the main problem. Replacing felts (praying no glue will spill on the carpet), greasing an ancient spring (praying it won't snap in your hands), all have to be done, but if you don't persevere and check everything, putting it all back together will have been a waste of time: there will be an improvement but the squeak, or the squeak that was hidden by the squeak you've just cured, will be all too evident to the customer who can no longer play the piano without having one ear trained on the pedals. To add to your injuries, rusted screws simply won't turn, so you find yourself flicking a lighter on and off to heat up the screw to loosen it. If it's an upright, you're practically crawling around in the bottom of the piano. If it's a grand (perhaps with a dodgy leg or two), you've the unnerving experience of crawling under something that has the potential to crush you like a sledgehammer splattering a melon (they weigh about half a ton). You try a drop of oil as well, and wonder if you should get up and search for newspaper to put down. No, carry on but you drop the hot lighter and curse at your blackened thumb just as the owner comes in for a minute. There you are crawling around like a four-legged animal or else crouched almost in a foetal position, seemingly about to set light to her pride and joy.

In the worst scenario, the rusted screw-head breaks off in your hand (which is now grazed because you slipped and banged it into the sharp bits of the strings that are attached to the iron frame), and you'll have to take the whole pedal mechanism away with you. With dishevelled hair, no feelings in your legs, you try to stand up and explain. She looks at your blackened, oily hands and wonders if her piano, with pedals now flopping in a sorry state, will ever be the same again. It was only a squeak, after all.

With the second example concerning pedals, I had in mind a case where they were actually working, but that didn't mean much to the owner. It sounded as though someone had their foot on the pedal all the time. There was an annoying echo on the upright in question, and all the strings were vibrating at once, making it sound like a street barrel organ. It was an old piano and I discovered the action had been left so that it was slightly ajar; the notes worked but the dampers were not quite resting on the strings. I was surprised the customer, an elderly ex-wrestler, of all things, could tolerate the din the piano made. It was easy to rectify, I merely tightened some securing bolts so the action was closer to the strings and the notes became much crisper and echo-free.

Having finished the tuning, 'Mr Wrestler' talked about his cauliflower ear (of which he was very proud), and went over the finer points of his career in the ring. I also managed to explain how I'd cured the constant echo in his piano. He was mildly grateful but eventually explained that he'd deliberately loosened the action bolts himself and wedged it so that the dampers were not quite on the strings. It turned out he was a diabetes sufferer and had had to have part of his leg amputated. He could no longer sit and play the piano in the conventional way (now that he had a false leg), nor could he comfortably operate the pedals; instead, he sat on a high stool with his false leg sticking out slightly to the side. With the action in its normal position and the pedals being redundant, the piano was far too quiet. He knew just how to get that reverberating 'foot down' sound and showed me so by undoing my work and proudly playing 'Let the great big world keep turning'. Wrongly interpreting my polite applause as overwhelming admiration, he reached into a drawer and handed me a pair of spoons. I was supposed to play these to his rendition of 'Maybe it's because I'm a Londoner'. "Piano tuner you may be, lad, but spoon player you ain't... well, not yet," he said as he plonked away on the newly tuned echoing piano.

I was useless at playing the spoons, but wanted my fee, so persevered. Not impressed, he gave me a quick demo himself and obviously had the knack, tapping the twin spoons up and down his arm, on his elbow and down onto his good leg. As an encore, he pulled out an old portable record player, the sort that used to be seen at every jumble sale, and accompanied himself alongside the Decca LP admirably, hobbling around his kitchen floor whilst the silver spoons ran up and down most of his body (I kept my distance). Fatigue put an end to the hobbling, but, resting on his stool, the rhythmic flashes of silver continued along with the tapping of his one good foot. I asked if he knew the song that went 'Money, money, money' (by Abba), but he hadn't heard of 'Abbot', nor did he take the hint. It was only when his home-help arrived that I managed to get my fee and escape.

My helpfulness with that customer had not been needed. In fact, he'd made me very late for my next customer, but I'd hopefully left him satisfied. It was perhaps a failing in me that I was very bad at communicating then. I suppose I hadn't actually seen what other piano tuners did when on call; my experiences of piano tuning had been largely based in workshop or institutional settings (schools and communal residences). Les Garrad and Lee had not emphasised the importance of customer relations or maybe just presumed it was obvious. Smiling, good manners, conversation and punctuality came more naturally to them.

I found, in the beginning, horrendous silences when it came to having a break for tea. My first faux pas had been to innocently but rather abruptly say no to any offer of tea or coffee. Although Jim and the older workers had liked a good brew, I still didn't drink tea or coffee a great deal. Detecting a surprised and sometimes wounded expression on many of my customers' faces, I soon realised that, for many, it was considered accepted practice to have a cup when it was offered. I wouldn't have minded this but found I had to wait an eternity for the good lady to leave the room after she'd brought it in. I would carry on tuning, waiting for the tea to cool and for her to go out. At last I could enjoy a custard cream and force myself to sip the tea. On hearing that I'd paused for a break, however, the lady would be in the room like a shot, cup in hand, sitting eagerly opposite me with great expectation. She seemed to ask pointless questions or say things that were unconnected with the piano: "Weather's on the turn, isn't it?" or: "Cleared up a bit now, don't you think?" Or, for variety, perhaps: "Can't stop long, have to put the veg on for Roy's tea in a minute." What she was doing, of course, was indulging in the art of small talk/light conversation; and all I was doing was answering yes or no.

In hindsight I can see that many of my customers were surprisingly tolerant and quite skilful at improving my social skills. In certain households they must have seen the look of puzzlement on my face when they asked me what type of tea I would like (did they mean Co-op or Sainsbury's?), but usually managed to recommend one without being patronising. Nor can I recall detecting more than a flicker of an eyebrow when I scooped four teaspoons of sugar into the cup. Some would apologise when making coffee: "Sorry it's only instant," being unaware that instant coffee was all I ever drank at home anyway. My palate, though, soon grew more accustomed to fresh coffee and Earl Grey tea (eventually having neither with sugar).

Using the toilet (bog, loo, WC, lavatory, depending on the client) could also be awkward, especially as I seldom needed it. Old chaps would ask me if I'd like to strain the greens, go upstairs, point Percy; I hadn't a clue what they were on about until they tried more vaguely familiar expressions: would I like to use the little boy's room… the small room upstairs (I had no idea there were children in the house, and what on earth was in the small room, had they a second piano?). Others asked if I'd like to spend a penny, to wash my hands, did I want to use the bathroom (did I really smell that bad?)... Sometimes house-proud ladies had loos like palaces; they were absolutely spotless, making one feel guilty for even using them. On the other hand, others doubled as storerooms, where one had to battle a route through the paraphernalia of the hoover, buckets, boots and coats (seemingly belonging to daddy bear, mummy bear and baby bear) and then make sure a foot was wedged near the door, as there was no lock. Only once was a lady client somewhat reticent when I asked to use the loo, which was in the bathroom upstairs. I couldn't understand her hint of sheepishness until I actually went upstairs. It had been a long hot summer, and the water restrictions for car washing and garden watering were in full force. Contrary to the advice broadcast, her bath was filled brimming with cool, clear water, as were an additional six new plastic buckets.

Being slow to initiate conversation in the early days, I soon got the hang of it and quite enjoyed chatting away. Many of the customers, mostly female, revealed character traits that I found interesting. It would be an exaggeration to say that I was a kind of psychotherapist, but many of the customer relationships had that sort of air of trust and neutrality about them. I was naturally interested in people who had lost partners (often partners I had never met), and the role of wives or husbands who stayed at home most of the day (I'm not sure what feminists are so worried about; in my experience an Englishman's home was his wife's castle! Money, decisions, who did the washing-up; it nearly always seemed to be controlled by the woman of the house. In some homes, no joke, it was the man who wore a pinny). Others were natural gossips. I'm not sure if they realised they were blatantly gossiping or perhaps they did and thought that that was their prerogative as the keeper of the home: a perk of the role or simply because they had the time in which to develop the skills involved – curtain twitching, embellishing a stale story, increasing a network of fellow rumour senders and receivers. And we mustn't forget that competitive edge: getting the news before one's neighbour, then putting it across in the time-honoured *News of the World* genre (the paper most of them would scorn and would not admit to buying).

One particular gossip discovered I shared the same doctor as her (a 'gossiper' can be defined as one who starts every other conversation with, "I'm not a gossip, but..."). This doctor-sharing gossiper filled me in on the new partner who had joined the practice. Next time I saw the customer I commented on the sudden loss of the new doctor (who had apparently joined another practice). My customer started with the traditional opening shared by those in the coven, "I'm not a gossip, but..." and proceeded to tell me how the new doctor had been getting her prescribing wrong, repeatedly arrived late for work and had had a blazing row with the other partner before being asked to leave at the end of the month. I didn't tell the customer that I also tuned my doctor's piano (doctors always seem to be into gardening and music) and that the new 'partner' was merely a colleague filling in before the successful applicant could take up her permanent role at the end of the month. There had been no blazing row; the temporary colleague had also been waiting to take up a position she now had at a surgery closer to her home.

It was this same customer who lived in an expensively furnished, though rather small, terraced house who perhaps had aspirations of living in a mansion. She proceeded to tell me all about the new music teacher at her daughter's school (a private one run by the Girls' Public Day School Trust). I also tuned pianos there so she attempted to ply me for tit-bits. In these situations I tend to say little, partly for customer confidentiality and partly to allow the gossip to fill me in with what I really know is usually a lot of nonsense. The music teacher hadn't been there long, so Mrs G regaled me with how the new teacher's predecessor was 'obviously a lesbian… always had her favourites… thankfully she's retired now'. The early verdict on the new music teacher (who was a doctor of music, apparently) was that she was brilliant but totally unreliable. Couldn't be trusted to take the kids to the park, let alone abroad.

She only had one daughter, did Mrs G, so led a very sheltered life: evenings were spent quizzing her daughter about her day at school, what the other mums were doing and, with pen at the ready, pouncing on her daughter's homework. How she loved to read her daughter's teacher's comments about her lovely daughter's homework (because it was done by Mum). When the daughter's choir went on a school trip to sing at a couple of venues in Italy, Mrs G was wild with excitement – what a wonderful opportunity it was for the children, and their Marigold would have her first chance at developing her independence.

From the interminable postcard collection and slideshows, I discovered that mother and father had apparently been in attendance at the concerts in Italy. They booked into the same hotel and followed the school coach in their car as it toured around the country. I know Italy pretty well now, having endured session after session with Mrs G and her slide projector. An attempt at changing the subject on the fourth or fifth visit, by throwing an interested glance towards the garden, nearly blew my cover.

As it turned out, 'the garden' wasn't much of a garden at all. Still, the topic of the garden paved the way for Mrs G to talk about her recent new neighbour. Mrs G walked me over to the window. Pointing at her neighbour's garden, she asked, "There, what do you think of that?" There was a hint of disgust on her face but I wasn't sure what she was talking about, and I wouldn't be one of her breed if I couldn't detect the obvious. No, I would be out of the club if I didn't come up with the right answer, but the garden looked like any other garden to me. I must have been missing something. Both gardens were tiny, hers possibly had a few more flowers. The other was slightly plainer but didn't seem to suffer from overgrown grass or dumped shopping trolleys. Luckily she couldn't restrain herself any longer and let out her frustration. Apparently the neighbours had been in for a month and hadn't, simply hadn't! touched the garden. It was an absolute tip and really letting the side down. I agreed wholeheartedly as she pointed out the 'debris and chaos', though I wasn't sure that we were both looking at the same garden. I was only thankful she hadn't seen any of the gardens where I lived (I lived in West Norwood – which the lively West Indian railway station announcer always shouted through the platform intercom as 'Whiss Narwoot, diss iss Whiss Narwoot'. Like many people who lived there, I said I lived in West Dulwich. West Dulwich was close by, but was to West Norwood what a Porsche convertible is to a Lada).

OPEN ROAD...

With time, my efforts at small talk had become quite polished, rather too polished, though I was terrible at being assertive. I had friends and colleagues who could say just what they wanted to say, no matter how curt it might seem when in the formulation stage. Whether on the phone or in person, they could somehow bring a conversation to a suitable close if they simply didn't want to hear any more. They might have felt the early pangs of boredom setting in, or have another pressing engagement, or not like the direction the conversation was going in, but with panache and without any hint of rudeness the other speaker would pick up the signal. My friends and colleagues could be off the phone or out the door – anyone's door – at the drop of a hat, and the speaker would be apologising profusely for having detained them. In the homes of certain customers I would be screaming internally for customers to leave me alone – not another photo album, don't tell me about your lumbago yet again – but I was trapped. My body language must have been set to attraction (or sucker). I had a sensitive ear for more than just tuning pianos, and was expected to listen sympathetically to symptoms, local and national politics, the alarming increase in the price of butter, why Jesus always forgives, and how the younger generation have never had it so good.

Some customers were excellent with paying the fee; they'd settle up straight away. I liked this, as it avoided my having to broach the subject. It might seem simple enough to ask for your fee but, to me, having been made to feel like a guest in someone's home, enjoyed a cup of tea and a chat, chats that after a number of years became more personal, asking for the fee seemed like demanding money with menaces. I found the subject of money slightly embarrassing; I'd leave it until as late as possible in the hope that it was on the tip of their tongue. When they were walking me down the garden path and opening the gate, chatting away and with no obvious sign of reaching for their wallet or purse, I would make things even more excruciating by bumbling something like, "Shall I send you an invoice?" I said it to indicate that there was no hurry in paying, a cheque in the post would be fine (though often, in the early days, it wouldn't be fine – I was relying on the cash payment that day). I wanted to save them some embarrassment, but only institutions and businesses expected invoices, so it sounded almost sarcastic. Now they were red and slightly humiliated as they realised I'd not really been listening to a word they'd said, only thinking of the money they owed. A next-door neighbour would see this man loitering with his case in the garden. The owner would be rushing into the house, the staring neighbour left wondering if I was the doctor or debt collector. "Why didn't you say? I left your money on the music shelf for you. Here it is, still in the envelope." They'd been discreet and reliable; I'd been clumsy.

I thought I was quite experienced now, after a decade or so of piano tuning under my belt, but I still encountered occasional pitfalls. Percy Samms was an elderly man; I grew to dread his six-monthly phone calls. I had some darling customers who were a joy to visit. Mr Samms was also – the first time – but in my keenness to show an interest in his background, I paved the way for a regular trap that I couldn't free myself from. I found it quite interesting visiting many different types of households. You can get a good picture of a person or family by the car in the drive, the decor, photos and pictures on the walls, books on the shelf. Mr Samms, a retired accountant of sorts, was getting on. He asked me how old I thought he was (always a sign that the asker is proud of their age). I hate such questions in case I'm miles out. Someone who you later find out is seventy and you estimate (at their invitation) to be eighty is bound to feel a little upset with your honest estimation, so you fall into the trap of playing ridiculously safe and saying they look about fifty-five when they don't. You then have to feign surprise when they tell you proudly that they are, in fact, sixty-five.

Now, Mr S had the furniture and photos befitting his generation. I saw an army photo and enquired about it. Yes, indeed, it was Sergeant Samms; he'd served in Aden and elsewhere. His tale of life in the Second World War was mildly interesting (though there was never any mention of medals or injuries). He'd also lived in the same part of south London I now lived in, and was able to describe how it used to be, how his amateur dance band had played in most of the pubs in 'the Elephant and beyond' (referring to the Elephant and Castle area).

His own upright piano had been shunted around his different abodes before landing up in a leafy part of Surrey. I was only twenty minutes late for the next call and, anyway, it had been interesting. The problem was, the next time I visited, Mr S had got it into his head that I looked forward to his lectures on the history of accounting, the changing face of the Elephant and Castle, and the recollections of the Second World War from an asthmatic corporal's (have I demoted him?) perspective. Because he had lived through it and done it, he *knew* that a 'young, intelligent chap like you' would be interested in his experiences. The snippets heard on the first occasion had been a little entertaining; the problem arose on subsequent visits when his opener would be, "Did I tell you about my time in Aden?"

Before I could get in with, "Yes. Three times, actually," he'd be off and my face and head would resemble the nodding dog once frequently seen on the back shelf of saloon cars.

If I did manage to get up and start tuning while Mr S was in full flow, it seemed rude to interrupt his lecture but it was certainly no deterrent. I would try to carry on but his monotonous voice was worse than any nagging housewife you could imagine (apologies to all those non-nagging housewives). Hints such as, "I've just got to finish the treble, won't be long," were answered with, "You carry on, lad," and he would carry on also. I occasionally compromised by tuning the notes as best I could and pretended I was listening to him by giving nods of the head and approving verbal responses such as: "Really?" or: "That's interesting." I knew this was risky, though, as it was just my luck he'd change the subject to the tragic death of his much-loved wife, and I'd be smiling or referring to the Nazis (thinking we were still on the subject of the war) and saying, "Death's just what such scum deserve, isn't it!"

Nearly every time I left Mr S's house I felt despondent. He'd kept me there under false pretences, really. I wasn't happy because, more and more, I'd had to leave some of the piano untuned as time had simply run out (even after allowing more time than usual on each visit). It became a vicious circle as each time I visited, the piano would be in a worse state than previously. I desperately wanted to leave the whole piano in tune but as his lovely wife had grown very hard of hearing, and seemed to just stay in her room (because the piano was 'her husband's department'), he needed more than ever someone to talk to. He could play the piano in a vamping sort of way, and so knew if it was badly out of tune, so that put pressure on me to try and get through it all and leave it in reasonable shape. What made it worse was that this appointment ate deeply into my morning availability, but he was being charged less than the going rate because, on the first visit, being a pensioner I'd deliberately charged him a lower fee.

Looking at the car (or cars) in the drive or the size of the house, one is tempted to adjust the fee accordingly. When it's obvious it's an OAP I will try to keep the bill right down. Trouble is, I'm very bad at putting my fees up anyway (though it is easier over the telephone: I usually kick myself if I have forgotten to mention it when making the appointment), and have found myself charging some people the same price as five or six years ago. There again, Mr S, like many other seasoned OAPs, knows the tricks of their trade. They've written the cheque out before you come, and hand it over with a buttery, "Here. I hope it's okay, I'm sure I can trust *you* not to put your prices up." They might as well have dated the cheque 1937. Other OAPs hope to stave off an increase in fee by serving you a plate full of sandwiches with your coffee. Many a time I've hidden these in my case because I'm not a great fan of white bread, margarine and fatty ham smothered in suspicious mustard. I've no intention of hurting customers' feelings so usually leave one on the plate. This shows I'm not greedy, and also wards off enthusiastic scurries into the kitchen in search of yet more fatty sandwiches.

I learnt my lesson over refusing tea once when I went to a new customer. By this stage, drinking tea or coffee day in day out, I was hooked and certainly couldn't leave my house without a morning cuppa. This lady was a new customer and, although she wasn't in any of the areas where I normally worked, she had been recommended to me by the shop where she'd bought the piano some time ago. It was a baby grand and, after suffering some water damage from a leak through the ceiling, had notes that would stick. This was mainly through the wood being very prone to swelling, shrinking and warping at every turn of the weather and/or a turn of her central heating thermostat. It was really one of those jobs where the piano shop didn't want to know about it; they were banking on me putting it right as she'd apparently had two other tuners to put it right and neither had totally cured the problem. I think she was at her wits end but remained stoical: it was yet another piano man come to fix her piano. She was courteous and went through her now well-rehearsed saga of the rogue piano's history. Once ensconced in the living room I set about taking the keyboard to bits. It was towards the end of a long day but I liked a challenge. There was nothing better than 'winning' customers; for the self-employed, confirmation of your ability is one of the best rewards. Good word of mouth keeps you in business; a tuner lives or dies by his tuning fork (or am I being a touch melodramatic!).

After only about six minutes I was fully engrossed in my work, carrying out a thorough examination. There was a cheery voice from behind: "Cup of tea?" I couldn't turn round just then as I had the keyboard perched precariously on my lap, so answered a cheery, "No, thanks." I just heard a murmured, "Oh," which hinted more of a, "Be like that, then," and looked round to see the perfect hostess leaving the room with a silver tray laden with cakes, napkins, tea pot and fine china cups. It had been one of those days when everyone had offered me tea and I'd drank cup after cup. The sight of her tea ensemble had brought forth a bursting bladder, but I had to call out that, yes, I would love a cup after all. She returned but the damage had been done. She'd gone to a lot of trouble and she knew that it had been unnecessary – the man was only being polite. Hopefully, her piano gave her no further problems. I've no idea as she never contacted me again. (She probably had me marked down as 'rude'.)

As mentioned earlier, the nice thing about being self-employed is you know you must be doing most things right if the customers continue to use you again and again. It always gives me doubts if you do a job and a year or two later you've not heard anything (if asked, I will give a customer a six-monthly reminder, but will not give reminders after the first one as some customers seem to see polite reminders as 'stalking'). They could have moved away, of course, but the thought that the job has gone to someone else always needles me. More often than not, I've been surprised that, even after two or three years (sometimes even longer), a customer rings up out of the blue, requesting my services. It turns out that they've not had anyone else, they've simply 'not got round to having it done again'. Like those who only go to the dentist when something has fallen out or the pain has become too excruciating, some customers wait until the piano breaks down before calling you out.

The problem is, it is usually cheaper to have it done regularly rather than leaving it a long while. If it is in a bad state the piano may have dropped in pitch and need two or more tunings to put it right, and require other repairs too. I advised a new customer that I had taken on in Chelsea that I would need to return to give the piano a second tuning (we call these rough and fine tunings). She had obviously not had it tuned for a long while and had lost her last tuner's phone number. She seemed to think that I was after extra work and that one tuning should be enough: that would cure everything. She wasn't impressed with my advice and declined to have me back. I was a little annoyed as the piano had been improved but was not fully in tune. A second tuning would iron out any faults missed in the first tuning and ensure that it would remain stable for half a year or more. If the piano teacher or another tuner had visited, no doubt they would put the poor state of the piano down to the last man, 'who wasn't very good'.

This lady's husband must have decided to take control, as he'd got hold of my number from someone at work. He rang me out of the blue a few weeks after I had first visited and asked me to tune the piano as: "We've just had a chap round recently but he wasn't very good, the piano's gone out of tune already."

It hadn't clicked until I arrived at the house and realised that he was part of the same family and I was in the home of the lady where I'd done a 'rough' preliminary tuning. The wife was in Scotland, so the husband had taken the morning off to sort out this domestic problem. I decided to say nothing and got on and tuned it. He was very obliging and explained that they'd more or less been ripped off by the last man. I merely looked quizzical and gave the piano the follow-up tuning which I had originally recommended to the man's wife. He tried it afterwards and deemed it to be very satisfactory. I think he was a little pleased that he'd found a 'better' man than his wife, and sought confirmation that pianos don't need to have two tunings (which I answered as vaguely as possible on this occasion). His logic (which did seem logical) was that if a man repairs your washing machine, you wouldn't expect him to come and do the same repair twice in a few weeks. Trouble is, tuning is not repairing. If you don't visit the dentist for years, it may take more than one routine visit to put everything right.

You always have the upper hand when customers call you. You are in demand; sometimes you are treated like royalty if you've got them out of a hole: the concert organiser thought someone else would get a piano tuner; the last man condemned the piano, you've just rescued it; it's not your area but you've driven across London and put the piano right in time for the party (you're even invited to stay!).

As alluded to earlier, the response can be different when you're phoning to make your regular six-monthly (or yearly) appointment. Now they are casual; it's not urgent. "But you were only here a month or two back, surely," or: "Can you call back after Christmas, we're a bit busy?" (you're phoning in early October, when it's due). You have to decide whether it's worth phoning or not. Some customers are very business-like and will even ring you if you don't ring them. There's no urgency but they like that regularity, security, and enjoy seeing you again: they expect a call in April, when the central heating is switched off, and in October, when it has been turned back on again.

Other piano owners, especially those in possession of newly acquired instruments, are conscientious to begin with and always close the door with an emphatic "Now, *do* ring us. We want to keep it in good nick. We're relying on you!" In some cases these words, after a year, have been totally forgotten. The piano hasn't exploded; it's still there. Or maybe their enthusiasm has waned now they realise that seven-year-old Norman is not going to enthral concert audiences across Mile End and beyond. To Norman, the piano is now crummy; he's thinking of taking up the saxophone instead. The phone conversation usually goes something like this: "Hello. It's Mr Turner, the piano tuner. You asked me to give you a—"

"Sorry, who?"

"Mr Turner. I tuned your piano for you last September and—"

"Oh... Can you hang on, you'd better speak to the wife." What they don't know is I can often hear their hushed conversations (sometimes yelled if the wife is upstairs and 'can't come down'): "Jan... *JAN!* It's that piano guy, Turnip."

"Well, you sort it out. I've got to get Norman to his saxophone lesson."

"What do you mean, *I've* got to sort it out? I don't even know the guy."

"Do *you* want to take Norman, then?"

"Hello... hello."

"Yes, I'm here."

"Sorry about that, Mr Tulip. My wife said she'd love you to come but can you wait until the end of January as we've a busy two months ahead?"

"No problem." I read between the lines and take this as a 'Don't ring us, we'll ring you'. Problem is, if they leave it a long time there is every likelihood that the bill will be higher than normal (people don't always appreciate the fact that pianos will eventually go out of tune whether they are played or not). When you do get to visit these long overdue customers and have a little moan about the state of the piano, they always turn the tables: "Why didn't you call us? You shouldn't have let us leave it so long!"

A small pleasure I enjoyed when answering the phone was being able to detect the owner's voice even after hearing the shortest of sentence openers. When picking the receiver up, I used to delight in hearing a voice the other end speaking just two or three words before I could chip in with: "Oh, hello, Mr Smith. How are you?" I couldn't possibly have known that he would call me on that particular day (though you'll see in a minute there are exceptions to this statement). I was just fortunate in being able to sift rapidly through my mental logbook of customers' voice mannerisms and could take a concealed delight in being able to casually answer the phone as if I'd known all along that they would be ringing me at that precise moment. The pleasure came in hearing the incredulous pause and flummoxed response that followed it. If I wasn't quite sure who it was (unusual) then of course I'd keep quiet.

I know some people are not great believers in ESP, but it seemed too frequent to be coincidence. When the phone rang, if I was in the mood my mind would be very attentive to those first vital clues as to who was on the other end, yet many was the time when I sensed who it was before they had actually spoken. In some instances I would have it on my mind that a customer would probably ring me, and they did. Alternatively, having rung a customer, they would remark that they had been talking about me or were going to ring me that same day. The doubters could say that they (the customers) and I could well have been thinking about each other as it was 'that time of the year' when the piano was due for a tuning. As mentioned earlier, some customers like routine: always have the piano done in the autumn and the spring, some even have it done in the same week each visit. Yes, on occasions they, like me, were half expecting the phone call. On the other hand, my precognition sensed who was on the line even when they weren't due for a tuning, or the call sometimes had nothing to do with my work. It wouldn't work every time, but seemed too frequent to be mere chance or coincidence. Rather like my first NHS medical number as an adult was 440: of all the numbers to be given, what are the chances of my being given the frequency known as concert pitch? (Musicians and piano tuners tune to A440 as the standard/accepted pitch – whether for concerts or not – and even the dialling tone on my BT landline, incidentally, is the frequency of A440.)

Miss Stone had been an elderly customer I'd inherited through Harrods. She lived in a small cottage on the outer limits of my tuning round, Limpsfield: a bit of a drive but nice because it got me out of London and its immediate suburbs. She had always seemed a bit aloof, leaving me to get on with it, just giving a hello and a goodbye, no tea or conversation. She closely resembled a rag doll: old woollen clothing, thin body, concave chest and straw hair, yet presumably she must have had some money, as she could afford Harrods' fees.

I don't think she was like one customer I had, whose name was Curtis. Or so I was led to believe. A nice enough lady, but her modest council flat in Plumstead seemed out of keeping with most of the clientele at Harrods. It was only after about five years that she 'confessed' that her name was, in fact, Green. It had been arranged that a friend – the real Mrs Curtis – who happened to work at Harrods would purchase the piano using her staff discount, and Mrs Green would then pay her back. The 'present' came with the usual free tuning Harrods gave to all new customers, and Mrs Green (under the guise of Mrs Curtis), not being able to find a local tuner, had decided to have the new piano maintained under a regular Harrods contract. Trouble is, she had visions of the Harrods Thought Police finding out that she wasn't the real Mrs Curtis and arresting her and/or confiscating her pride and joy. The easiest thing to do was to keep up the pretence that she was the name that appeared on the invoice. After a few years she felt it no longer necessary to cruelly deceive the innocent and hard-working piano tuner. It explained to me why, when in the early days I used to ring her, she always hesitated and sounded rather puzzled – I felt like saying, "Look either you're Mrs Curtis or you aren't. If I've got the wrong number, just say so."

Returning to the rather scrawny Miss Stone of Limpsfield, like a few of the Harrods customers I inherited, she was the last person you'd think would have anything to do with Harrods. I think such clientele either used Harrods because it was the easiest way to get a piano tuner (it didn't involve them having to visit the actual store) or else the piano was such an important possession that they felt it had to be maintained by a 'big-name company'. In reality it meant they were paying well over the odds and receiving a service that was not likely to be any superior to one offered by a more local freelance tuner. Indeed, with some customers it was always difficult not to take up their occasional offer of them paying me cash direct and knocking out the middle man. It was tempting on both sides, as I would receive direct payment that was slightly higher than Harrods actually paid me for each tuning (due to the commission Harrods took), and the customer would still be paying less than they were currently paying Harrods (like Mrs 'Curtis', it was me in fact who was green at the time, as I had visions of the Harrods Thought Police finding out that I was stealing their customers. In hindsight, I don't think they could have cared one way or the other).

With Miss Stone, I don't know how but, by accident, after many visits we somehow got round to talking about spiritualism just as she was signing the appointment card prior to my leaving the house. It had been like a light bulb moment and from then on I always had a cup of tea from Miss Stone. She would talk endlessly about spiritualism and her interest in the Swedenborg Society. I became quite fascinated and went along to spiritualist churches by myself. I found that, as no doubt many others have found, you don't really get much that is convincing. I do believe in it, but unless you're dealing with the few people at the top of the business, the 'messages' can be mildly comforting and relevant (amid all the false starts and 'crossed lines'), but rarely come up to expectations. The spiritualist churches, too, are a strange phenomenon. Claiming to be Christian, and having many of the usual hymns and prayers of a church, many other Christians dismiss them as playing with the devil. Newcomers only go through all the long-winded service and painful hymn singing in the hope that the guest medium will single them out with a message at the end. What disappointment if they don't! It's perhaps quicker and better to pay a fee and have a private reading. These are invariably more accurate, though I suspect they butter up all their clients (as they did me) by saying, "You have a lovely aura around you. Are you sure you don't have the gift?"

Miss Stone eventually had to give up her cottage and went into an old people's establishment – one of a slightly better class than I had previously seen. As I was in the area I visited her once soon after she'd moved in. It was clean and comfortable, but how quickly the residents lose their independence and former identities. She offered me a cup of tea – the 'ceremony' we'd began to enjoy together in my later visits, along with a chat – but she was a bit naive to think that she could use her own cups and saucers at her new home. "If you'd asked me beforehand, Dot,

I would have let you. Tea comes round at four, darling, but I'll get you and your visitor a cup this time." The carer seemed firm but polite. Miss Stone, I suspected, felt embarrassed and rather helpless.

Miss Stone had agreed (without any qualms!) that she would make every effort to contact me once she was on the other side. To date, not even a whisper. How disappointing. If the enthusiasts can't even get through, how genuine is it all? I would have loved to have made contact with Mr Garrad. He was a devout Christian, and so presumably wouldn't have approved, so it would have been a lovely turn up for the books if he'd come to give me a message, even if it was, "You need to go to church more, instead of playing with all this hocus-pocus."

What I consider a good test in these matters involved a long-established private day school housed in a large Victorian house. The old caretaker lived there and, it being the half-term holiday, generally liked to hover and have a chat while I worked away. He said that one room of his flat, which was at the top of the school, was definitely haunted. When they came to stay, family members had refused to sleep there more than once, after waking up to find a heavy weight on their bed and a feeling of being smothered. I can't say I felt any bad vibes myself, though older schools can be a spooky place when you're in there all alone. The caretaker eventually passed away. One term I met the young wife of the new caretaker, who let me in. She'd obviously not met the old caretaker and knew little about the school. I asked her how she was settling in. Okay apparently, but she would never ever sleep in one particular room. She described a feeling of tightness and being smothered in the night. It had been their idea to make it a long-term placement, as the job seemed ideal, but they had both decided to move on as soon as possible. Just a year or two later the school suffered a serious fire in the top of the building and had to be virtually rebuilt, but I had lost contact by that stage.

Talking of making contact, a colleague of mine had a terrible stutter and, though he earned his living as a piano tuner, was also a very talented pianist. Having a good musical ear, he was in the habit of avoiding 'nuisance customers' he was expecting to phone him, by answering the telephone in a heavy Irish or Welsh accent. When singing or putting on an accent, his stutter disappeared marvellously. If it was the terrible Mr Briggs who always haggled over the price and allowed his two dogs to yap away non-stop, my tuning colleague, at the first detection of it being Mr Briggs, would answer accordingly: "...6414, Evans here."

"Oh, erm... is that the piano tuner?"

"No peeano twoner here, boyo. Yuve obbveeoosly got the wrong number."

The said colleague was also in the habit of wearing gloves when tuning pianos. This might have looked a bit strange, but continuously striking the piano keys using a firm action puts considerable wear and tear on the hands and fingers. The keys have to be struck fairly hard if the string is to stay in tune for a reasonable length of time (otherwise the piano can be 'knocked out of tune'). The actual art of piano tuning, in some ways, is a mechanical, methodical business that is quite unmusical. My colleague would do anything to protect his precious fingers.

I too looked after my fingers, but wasn't *that* sensitive about them. I did once convince a customer that my ears were insured for £8,000 each. Some customers are gullible. Another one informed me proudly that her last piano tuner's father, also a piano tuner, had actually selected the tree and cut it down so that it could be used in the building of her piano. I couldn't tell her, but it was one of the cheapest, shoddiest mass-produced baby grands that ever existed. It had what's known in the trade as a transfer name. Literally, because it was a non-entity piano, made by one of several firms that (at that time) would knock out cheap pianos for any high-street retailer or department store keen to exploit the piano's popularity, any name could be stencilled onto the finished woodwork.

German-sounding names were often used for these cheaper pianos as they gave an air of craftsmanship and quality; alternatively, an illusion of grandeur was deployed by other retailers to give a hint of better-known piano manufacturers. For example, 'Steinbech' meant it was neither the well-known Steinway nor its rival Bechstein, but helped to conceal the fact that it was a bog-standard Brown and Sons, built in a backstreet factory in the Old Kent Road. (I think it was Bruce Forsyth who always seemed to enjoy coming on stage and courteously announcing: "Steinways have asked me to announce that the piano is a Bechstein.") I once had a rather boastful and know-it-all customer who suggested his German piano was 'most probably one of the best on your list, isn't it?' It was a Blüthner – a fine, solid make – but some of a certain vintage are well known for their inherent defects and for not being good pianos at all. I asked him if he knew much about the name Blüthner, and surprisingly he didn't. Keen to trawl more facts, presumably for his long-hoped-for appearance on *Mastermind*, I told him it actually meant butcher. He seemed disappointed. (I don't suppose his disappointment will last forever, as it doesn't really mean butcher at all; it's just a family surname.)

When the lady told me about the tree story, I guess she could see I wasn't convinced, so she pointed to the Gold Medal Awards that could just about be seen symbolised under the strings, on the soundboard. It was pretty dusty and she insisted on practically crawling into the piano with a torch to show me the 'rare and hard-earned' accolades. I hadn't the heart to tell her that these too were meaningless transfers used to give the image of tradition and expert craftsmanship. In fact the dates depicted on the transfers pre-dated that piano and could have been referring to any model or firm. To her mind she was sitting on a goldmine, convinced it would fetch thousands at an auction. I tried to let her down gently, but perhaps some people have to learn the hard way.

Other customers had pianos that, if not of great value, had a bit of history behind them. Miss Tewkes had a large Steinway upright that had once sailed the ocean waves (she reeled off a long list of famous pianists who had apparently played on it). Her Steinway had come from a fine liner (the *Queen Mary*, I believe); evidence could be seen in the enormous feet at the bottom of the piano, which still had large round holes where the piano had once been bolted to the floor in case it toppled over during a rough passage (sea not musical).

Miss Tewkes had the strange skill of perfect pitch. Lee the blind tuner also had it, though the majority of piano tuners don't. Some tuners, who are also musicians, do not always enjoy the gift, as they find it irritating when instruments are tuned to the 'wrong' pitch. It must also be strange sometimes, as Lee told me that everything, be it a hoover in operation or a squeal from a tyre, all emit a musical pitch which is as recognisable to those with perfect pitch as colour is to others. Miss Tewkes, however, told me that she had learnt that it was necessary to adjust her perfect pitch as she got older. If Miss Tewkes was in the other room and I played a note on the piano (any note at all), she could tell me exactly what note I was playing. But she explained that, for some reason, over the years she had somehow acquired the 'wrong' perfect pitch: she began to find out that she was consistently a semitone out, so she always allowed for this. If she heard the note that, to her, sounded like C sharp, in order to get the right answer she knew she would have to call out the note D. The piano was always tuned to concert pitch but her perfect pitch, for some reason, had shifted down a semitone in later life, so she had to compensate for this.

I mentioned bad customers earlier; sometimes it can be the case that the customer is a lovely person but, unknown to them, they've got a stinker of a piano (it's quite nice to play but is a nightmare to tune). I've often wondered if doctors see their patients by their medical condition rather than by name. Dog owners are said to resemble their pets: A. F. Hound, who has a prominent nose and long, smooth hair. Does the doctor see patient X as the liver man, or Mrs B as Mrs HRT? Piano tuners tend to use the word 'with' quite a lot: Mrs Andrews with the Steinway model O; or Jim Peters with an overstrung Collard, the one with the buzzing bass; Miss Smithers, she's got a Bechstein with a cracked frame – thinks it's a marvellous piano.

Some pianos are a nightmare to tune; they can try the patience of a saint. It might be that the tuning pins click and jump, and just won't stay where you'd like them to stay, or certain strings (through an inherent design fault) sound false. No matter how well they've been tuned, the quality of the notes simply sound terrible. Such pianos I hate tuning and yet their owners can be a pleasure to visit. When they ring up, the dreadful piano looms into my imagination (for example, it always seems to take twice as long to tune Mr Meadow's piano than most other pianos); it haunts me immediately. Most times, the customer is quite oblivious to the fact that they own a problem piano. I guess some even imagine I enjoy tuning them as, to all intents and purposes, I appear to be spending a lot of time and care on it, which is obviously a sign that it is worth doing so on such a good instrument. It's taking me a long time because it won't stay in tune, it's a horrid piano, keeps falling apart and no matter how hard I work, to me it sounds little better even after I've slaved away for an hour and forty-five minutes on it!

As my career progressed I was fortunate in getting more and more Harrods work as their full-time tuners were obliging enough to retire or die off. In addition to my already extensive range of clientele I now had the elite end of the market. From climbing the rickety stairs of Nurse Morris in rundown Peckham, I found myself driving through electronic gates and down private drives longer than the main road where I lived. Returning to Nurse Morris for a moment, she was an odd woman: a petite hospital nurse who was always at home 'ill'. She'd been in London a long time but her Irish accent still came through. It was probably the long climb up the dark, narrow staircase that led to her tiny attic room home that made her ill. As I say, she wasn't strong, and rented this dreary room at the top of an old, draughty house. Like a rabbit in a hutch, her room consisted mainly of chewed carpet, a sofa bed and one table which contained papers and pills, along with lettuce leaves and tomatoes for her meal of the day.

Being a nurse, she was good at describing her condition to me. I suggested more light and air might help, but she shuddered; air, apparently, spread diseases. I'd hinted at fresh air on one particular occasion because I was nearly knocked out from the smell of industrial paint. Being near the clouds in this dim bedsit, I'd overlooked the fact that there seemed to be a distinct absence of windows. It was when I attempted to take the mini-piano (and it really was one of those tiny mini-pianos) to bits that I discovered a problem. Nurse Morris, off work due to what she diagnosed as acute gastro-enteritis (tummy ache), had decided to cheer herself up by obtaining some cheap NHS yellow emulsion from someone at King's College Hospital. She'd liberally painted the walls of her room and, not wanting to carry unused or half empty cans back downstairs, she'd slapped it liberally all over her mahogany piano to 'brighten it up'.

The piano, apart from a few nicks and scratches, didn't need a face-lift of this sort. It was a lovely mahogany colour but she felt that a hint of yellow in the room wouldn't only brighten it up but add value to the instrument as well. Here and there one could see some interesting yellow rivulets on the piano's casing. There were also some bulbous blisters that had a custard skin texture, but the bulk of her handiwork had set firm. Sadly, it didn't occur to her to first remove the parts and paint them as separate items. The lid and its once shiny, chromed hinge were frozen in time, refusing to give at all. The other panels and music desk had set nicely too, resulting in a wrestling match between this matchwood piano and an annoyed piano tuner getting high on paint fumes. Struggle as hard as I might, the innards of the piano could not be penetrated. Nurse Morris was more worried about my undoing her artwork than it being howling out of tune. Her pulse, apparently, wasn't allowed to get thready. I thought it best to call back another day with a hammer and chisel (praying she'd lose my telephone number in the meantime). Ring she did. If only I could put her off the scent by using a good Irish accent. (No, not Irish. She'd keep me talking and would spot a fake Irish accent a mile off.)

Entering the exclusive St. George's Hill estate and other such places, I could see how the other half lived. St. George's, where I had a few clients, had its own tennis and golf clubs, also a swimming pool and luxury spa. In addition to the numerous millionaire Russian residents, the estate, known as the Beverley Hills of Surrey, was also home to the likes of Cliff Richard, Ringo Starr and Kate Winslet. You couldn't get into the place without passing the peaked cap security personnel, who would then keep an eye to make sure you or anyone else wasn't parking on any of the roads (if you were there on business, you'd park in someone's driveway). It was always a lovely drive, nonetheless, eyeing up the splendour of each residence as I made my way to the right home. Bentleys and Rolls Royces were almost everywhere; there were only ever two or three people letting the side down with their two-year-old Mercedes. All the homes had the putting green lawns, sprinklers and swimming pools you'd expect. Some had two swimming pools. I wouldn't have been surprised if some of the inhabitants had three.

With money littering the place, the joke once told me by an inebriated customer who stalked me whilst I worked on a pub piano might have rang true here. He insisted on telling me his joke, no matter how loudly I banged on the piano keys.

"Why have you got three swimming pools?" asked the new gardener.

"Simple! One's got cold water. That's for the summer, when the kids like to have a good splash around most days. The other's got warm water; it's an indoor one and we do a serious bit of swimming during the winter months."

"What about the third one, then?"

"Oh, that's empty."

"Why is it empty?"

"Because it hasn't got any water in it."

"Yes, but why hasn't it got any water?"

"It's for guests who can't swim."

I was nearly drowned in his raucous laugh and alcoholic vapour.

Tuning pianos in pubs always made my heart sink. You either had to do them just before opening times, when early punters would be knocking on the door or actually ordering the first round of drinks (so you had to contend with polite/impolite conversation, the jukebox or background music), or else you tuned the piano when the pub was closed. This usually meant you had competition: the strains of your efforts versus F sharp on a Dyson hoover. And pubs are always such dim places, where you can't see what you're doing and the piano has inevitably been the victim of physical abuse, and been fed a diet of unwanted crisps, cigarette butts and stale beer.

So calling at a small though well-known private club in the West End for the first time, I wasn't optimistic. Quite anonymous on the outside, it was a drinking club used by major and less major actors appearing in local theatres, as well as other famous regulars. Banging hard on the heavy metal door, it buzzed open. I left the thronging tourists heading for Carnaby Street, they were enjoying rare late September sunlight; I, in turn, descended some dank and steep steps. I pulled open another door and was met with blackness. Bumping into chairs and tables, I felt my way around the walls and chairs – was this a set-up, was I about to be mugged? – hopefully not, I thought whilst following the distant voice of the manager. Like a pit pony, I was led over to the piano, which I could just about make out, now that my eyes had adjusted to the conditions a little. As an afterthought, he asked if I wanted the lights on (he was working in a back office before opening time). I was optimistic but this only produced a slightly higher candle wattage than before, so I proceeded to open up the piano and get started as best I could. Despite the stained and mucky keyboard, surprisingly it was quite a new instrument, though the wear and tear dated it by about twenty years. It had certainly been knocked about a bit: in addition to the chunks of missing woodwork, there was evidence of numerous replaced broken strings (very rare in fairly new pianos), and a heavy sprinkling of cigarette ash. The manager said that Jerry the pianist was hoping to drop in and see me if he could (Jerry indeed; I'd like to have a word with this Jerry – why isn't there something equivalent to the NSPCC for abused pianos?).

After an hour and a half of hard slog, the piano was ready. Just as the manager handed over the money and I felt keen to nibble the grass on the surface, good timing (the manager thought) saw the regular pianist enter: he could have come in at any time, why now, just as I was leaving? He greeted me with a cloud of smoke and a firm mafia-type handshake (or was he a freemason?). I wasn't impressed; his yellow fingertips and veiny face told me who was the likely abuser of this poor instrument. He didn't have to be asked to try it out; as an alcoholic can't stay away from the grog, he had to satisfy his piano withdrawal symptoms. Sceptical, I withheld my intended lecture to the manager and so-called pianist on piano etiquette and maintenance, and gazed around at the signed photos on the walls. Ronnie Scott, Dicky Attenborough (darling Dicky) and pics of many others who were 'in the bizz' could have been slipped into my briefcase (as compensation for emotional distress) if they hadn't been nicely but firmly screwed to the walls.

Jerry, this hacking pianist, was not a face or name I knew. In fact, as he proceeded to run up and down the keys, he hadn't even removed his cigarette from his pursed lips. I'd just cleaned those keys! But my contempt transformed into admiration as I sank into a deep leather sofa that lined one wall and listened to the jazz that exuded from every note, string, fibre and particle that made up that piano. I wasn't a great fan of jazz but Jerry, who couldn't give two ***** whether anyone was listening or not, swiftly mesmerised me with his playing. It sounded like three people were playing that piano (or a musical octopus perhaps). And I could see why strings had broken in the past: his performance was very physical – aggressive in places – with karate-style chopping in the bass. He was in the process of slaughtering that piano, yet it made great music. I left him happy, and me happy: the manager offered me a monthly contract to keep it in tune. A great musician and a great guy, that Jerry.

Half the time when visiting the homes of Harrods' customers I would never see the owner. He or she would be on the golf course, in town shopping or at the office. The 'servants' would show me in and help clear the piano (always much more helpful than most of the actual owners). The servants went under the euphemism of cleaner, maid, au pair, nanny or simply 'Maria' (or whatever their first name happened to be). Maid was a common term when children weren't involved, and most seemed to be Spanish or Filipino, though a younger breed was emerging from eastern

Europe. Of course, they were not servants because they weren't from the Victorian or Edwardian period. For some, coming from a poor background, the guaranteed full-time employment and somewhere to live was something to be grateful for. There was also no hint of envy; many seemed to accept their position in life: a preordained role. The fine objects in the house, from treasured antiques to state-of-the-art technology, silverware in the dining room and opulence in the loo, sorry, lavatory, could be savoured during the long periods when madam was 'out', which often meant, if not shopping, she was at the gym or spa/salon. Although it wasn't theirs, to be living in an exclusive area, touching, seeing and breathing the plushest of deep-pile carpets and chic furniture, seemed more than enough.

Once, being rather lazy, I hadn't looked too carefully at the address on the new customer card sent by Harrods. I should have known better as names such as Egerton often have such variables as Egerton Square, Egerton Mews, Egerton Street and Egerton Terrace. On this particular hot day I headed towards what I thought was the right number in the right road. As usual, a Filipino let me in. She was new but I was half-way through the tuning before I decided to look at the card again. Something in her initial expression and the unfamiliar surroundings had prompted a doubt in my mind. The card told me I'd got the right number but wrong road. It was Egerton Square I needed, not Egerton Terrace. Here I was tuning a stranger's piano without their permission! Worse still, I wouldn't get paid for it and I would be late for the genuine appointment. It wouldn't have been easy to explain to the maid, so I finished off and hurriedly put the piano back together. "You quick! You want tea?" I don't know why but I always seem to respond in a kind of pidgin English in these situations. Smiling meekly, I answered, "Me not thirsty, thank you, I go now." She looked at me strangely: "No poblem, I tell Miss, sir," and closed the door.

HARRODS LTD. S.W.1			Instructions	
Name				
Address			Style of Instrument	
Telephone			No.	
Date	Remarks	Customer's Signature	Technician's Signature	
1701A				

9. An unused Harrods appointment card.

The appointment cards used by Harrods could be used to send reminders of appointments, but were more usually brought each time a tuner visited. I rarely bothered to sign them myself and, if it was a regular customer, I never got them to sign it (the tuning office didn't ask to see these cards). I was rather unsure what the 'Remarks' column was for; there wasn't much room to say anything, but was I supposed to comment or the customer? It could have given the customers the opportunity to be condescending or critical ('satisfactory' or 'late!', perhaps), but I don't recall any customers actually entering anything in this column.

Not all maids lived at home. Some did domestic service for pin money, others to get their children through a private school. In some cases, however, where the worker has been recruited in the employer's country of origin (or through an agency which 'knows its clients' needs'), terms and conditions seem to rely on verbal statements, or at least don't conform to any British law. On the surface, these employees are not mistreated, though I gained a truthful insight into their lifestyle when sent to do a free tuning for a new Harrods customer.

I remember visiting this Arab family who lived a stone's throw from the Royal Albert Hall. The thick mahogany door was opened by a tiny Arab girl wearing an apron (she was probably eighteen or nineteen but looked much younger). "It's the man from Harrods," she called down the corridor in something barely stronger than a whisper. Within a few minutes, the lady of the house arrived and took over. She was charming and showed me to the newly parked piano. I said 'house', though it was actually a large, expensive Kensington apartment. We walked along seemingly miles of twists and turns to get to the music room. On the way, fresh-cut flowers in crystal glass vases marked off entrances to various rooms. Be it the pool room, guest room or one of the numerous bedrooms, they were all lined with plush wallpaper, deep carpets and gold fittings. It would seem I was exaggerating, but most of the rooms were lit by glinting chandeliers.

Some fifteen minutes later, having settled into the job in hand, the lady came to offer me a cup of tea, which I gladly accepted. In my naivety I thought she would make it herself, but it arrived some six minutes later in the hands of (this time) a male domestic (I'm not sure how he would officially title himself). He was very dutiful and asked me if I would like anything else. He hovered in the background with a duster while I continued. It's always a bit eerie when someone is half looking over your shoulder, but he was young and flashed a keen smile whenever I looked his way. It turned out that he was to inform madam when I had finished. Thus, at the appropriate time, he slipped away and madam returned. A generous tip of ten pounds was placed in my hand (tips were not that common, but two or three pounds, five at the most, was the norm then) and I was shown to the lift.

Satisfied with my work, the owners requested my future services through Harrods' piano-tuning department. Like all their clientele, a contract was taken out and I found myself appearing at the apartment at regular six-monthly intervals. As the owner had quickly grown accustomed to my phone calls and visits, there were occasions when she'd be out of the house while I was working (the novelty factor of seeing 'the craftsman at work' had passed on). On such occasions I couldn't help pushing Abdul (we'll call him), the male servant, to open up a little. I was fascinated with the paradoxes in his life: living alongside such opulence but not really able to take part. Having a secure job and seemingly kind employers, but where did he live? At the top of the apartment, he said. Where was his family? Back home. It was difficult to get straight answers from him; this was not because he wanted to misinform me, I sensed it was because of a certain tension that existed in the relationship with the family, and that I might say the wrong thing to madam, perhaps. He was part of the family, had watched the children grow up to become Cambridge undergraduates, but madam was his employer. It was perhaps truer to say that he was merely part of the household. I felt that he was holding back, though in his efforts not to actually lie I felt that some of the truth naturally came through.

What were his hours? Oh, there were no hours, they were not servants in that way. Well, could he go out when he wanted to? Of course, he assured me, though in a second breath he seemed to remind himself as well as me that he could only go out with madam's say so, and that was after all the jobs had been done. It was his duty, along with the maids, to prepare breakfast (and all meals), do the daily cleaning of the house from top to bottom, valet the car, let visitors and tradesmen in. But what about in the afternoon – there were several staff, so couldn't he go out then? Well, yes, he could go out anytime, but if madam was out shopping, he had to be around so as to help load up the car or carry things back to the apartment (their 'corner shop', of course, was Harrods). I was puzzled at this implied air of freedom which didn't really seem to exist, but remembered that I too had to work every day. At least he had the evenings off. What did he do in the evenings?

It sounds like an interrogation on my part, but we were of a similar age, and while I was in the kitchen having a cup of tea, I was also filling him in (occasionally!) on how my days and weeks were spent. It hadn't fully occurred to me that while I'd been sipping my tea and chatting away, he'd been working the whole time while answering questions. One ear and eye had been scanning the door entry camera in case madam returned home early, whilst his hands had been deftly throwing ingredients into bowls, mixers or onto trays ready for the oven. Pristine utensils were to hand in this showcase kitchen. I was quite envious of his creative skill, but this was no afternoon hobby. Reading between the lines, this was a daily grind. Madam insisted that all meals be made from fresh ingredients. It was a never-ending conveyor belt and a matter of planning ahead, keeping a stock of homemade meals always to hand. It was made all the more demanding because the children might look in whilst in London, or madam might decide to have friends over. The other half of the challenge was the debris left after: mountains of washing up, cleaning down and leaving things ship-shape for breakfast early the next morning.

I asked Abdul if he missed his family, which he did. I wondered if he got a chance to see them when madam made trips back to the homeland (imagining free flights might be a perk of the job). He said this was very rare as, when madam went away, it was important to keep a residual staff in the apartment for security, to answer calls, keep it clean, and let service people in when necessary. As he sifted a white, milky concoction through his fingers (and still flashing an optimistic smile), I commiserated and half joked that at least he could have parties and entertain while the family were away for these long holidays. It wasn't parties that interested him; he'd prefer to go with them. It was boring when the apartment was empty and, if anything, harder work, as this was the time when it would either be redecorated or thoroughly spring cleaned so as to be in perfect condition for madam's return. I couldn't help wondering if madam had an obsession with cleanliness, or was it a ploy to keep the workers shackled? Being young and rather blunt, I asked him why he didn't look for another job. Here, for the first time, a flash of real hope spread across his face. He told me that he was making plans to attend a college on his one night a week off. He had hopes of doing computing or accounting, something that would lead to his dream of a new career. In the meantime he was not without clothes and food, and his employers never hit him.

SUNSET YEARS

It took me quite some time to realise that certain of my Harrods customers were unsure of themselves – it was they who lacked experience or confidence. To start with I had been in awe of my new clientele and their surroundings. A few were even well-known politicians and actors (which I'll come to). To others, the Kensington and Knightsbridge set, they were all part of an exclusive village – though a village that was largely deserted at the weekends when they retreated to their country homes nestled on the borders of real villages. These people were paying nearly twice the going rate for a tuning, but it was convenient; all they had to do was sign my card and everything would be taken care of. Lord Hi-Faluting or the Hon Mrs Madrich-kow: I grew accustomed to these barons of Brompton.

Some of the lesser fry on my Harrods list, with some money but no title or fame, unconsciously let it slip from time to time that they realised they were low on the pecking order. They'd apologise for having a mere upright rather than a grand (presuming most of my customers owned grand pianos or that I'd be somewhat snobbish about having to tune a mere upright), yet most new good quality uprights still cost thousands of pounds – at the time of writing, around £12,000 for a good quality (but not top-of-the-range) upright. If they probed me about my client list, I'd either be evasive and hide behind the (largely imaginary) cloak of ethics and client confidentiality, knowing it would make the customer even more curious and insecure of their own position on the ladder of status, or I'd name drop with an apparent air of boredom (as though it were difficult to know where to start). "Whose that chap who stars in *Only Fools and Horses*?" Before they could answer I'd be in with the next name: "And... the chap who was on *Question Time* last night, he's in the Shadow Cabinet, isn't he?" The customer would enthusiastically help me out: "Yes! I saw him. He's the Defence Minister. What piano has he got?"

"Oh, I tuned his only last week. Lives in Fulham, though has a place in Wiltshire too, of course. He can't play a note. It's for Samantha and Jeremy, the children... when they're home from Eton... Nice piano, though, a white Schimmel grand... Though that film director, Forbes, Bryan Forbes, he's got two pianos. We got his contract after Steinways let him down..."

New 'unknown' customers were often unsure whether they should – or were allowed to – tip you or not, and I was never sure (the people in the pianoforte tuning and valuation department – in reality a grubby little office with two members of staff, hidden on the top floor of Harrods – knew absolutely nothing about pianos and couldn't advise on social conventions. Provided they didn't get any complaints from customers, they considered you a 'good' tuner). Some customers did tip, most didn't, though some would give you a bottle of something at Christmas. One or two were very cordial in other ways: allowing me to park my car in their drive, any time I wanted to visit the Wimbledon Tennis Championships (the club was just down the road). Another had what looked like a delightful rustic holiday home in the back of beyond up in Scotland. It contained a piano which they could get no one local to tune. If I fancied tuning it, I could have a free holiday up there any time. It was tempting but too far for my liking.

It was always difficult to handle tipping situations. The seemingly more worldly-wise customers were able to tip you in a natural, smooth way. The worker-employer relationship wasn't there at all (even if some of the older houses in Chelsea did have separate servants' and visitors' bells at the front door). You were treated as a friend, and a few pound coins or some folding money would be slipped into your hand along with a handshake when it was time to leave. No fuss. I didn't expect a tip and treated it as a nice bonus when it came. It only became awkward when new customers had obviously been deliberating. Whilst I'd been tuning they had been pondering: should I tip or not? Would it be a faux pas if I didn't? What does he expect to be reasonably generous? If I tip this time, will I have to tip every time?

The few well-off foreign customers settled in London generally found it harder to conform. One, an American wife of a well-known writer of TV sitcoms, never perfected the art, even after several years of practice. She would come in after hearing my tell-tale closing arpeggios. Concealed in her moist hand was a tip. I could see a glint of money as she transferred it nervously to her other hand so that she could hold a pen to sign my Harrods visiting card. "Thank you. I'll be off then." I'd wait a second or two, the cue for the handover, but she would stand there dumbstruck. Having said I'd be off, I would pick up my case and edge towards the door (now, with car keys in one hand and case in the other, a handover would be less than smooth). She seemed to want to say something or mention the tip but always spoke in erratic spurts (whereas earlier she'd been fine when letting me in or offering me a cup of 'corfee'. Had even joked, asking if I wanted leaded or unleaded, meaning with or without caffeine). "Erm, how was it, the piano?"

"Not too bad." If a second question came I'd have to put the case down and chat: I hate it looking as though I'm always wanting to get out as fast as possible.

All I really wanted was for her to either hand over the tip or let me go, not keep me in this state of limbo. "I'm sure Delilah will be so thrilled now the piano's bin tooned. She can always tell when you've bin."

"That's nice to hear." I can't stand there with a heavy case lengthening my arm, so I put it down. She dries up and expects me to say something. I make something up: "I gave it a bit of a dusting inside, needs it occasionally." Now I've distressed her: "Oh… did you want the hoover? Was it *that* dusty? You should have asked, the hoover's just under the stairs here, I'm not sure how it works but…" It looks as though I'm touting for more money or inferring that she keeps an untidy home. "No, no, it's all taken care of. Only took a matter of minutes." Silence again. "Right. I'd best be off. Don't want to be late for my next appointment." Now she flusters. "Of course… erm, here, a little something for you." I have to feign surprise, though how surprised and grateful I'm supposed to look, I don't know (it's only two pounds, it's always two pounds). On her part there's an audible sigh of relief. Tip over, she's relaxed and is quite happy to stay and chat now. I have to show a morsel of gratitude as I stealthily edge towards the front door. We part on good terms, but this stress occurs every time, my pretending to be surprised and grateful for the tip, and her never improving the handover (if only her script writer husband had been spying the scene, he might have been able to work it up into something useful for TV – *The Wrong Chord* or *Bum Notes*?).

It hadn't really twigged at first that some of my customers were likely to be famous. The first one didn't register when I saw the name on the card (Harrods sent copies of new contracts and appointment cards through the post). It was a Mrs Stubbs, which turned out to be the actress Una Stubbs. Another was Mr Hopkins of Eaton Terrace, which turned out to be the London home of the former Dr Treves and Mr H Lectern (the actor of).

There was no guarantee that such people would be at home, of course. Often it was a partner or housekeeper who let me in. Anthony Hopkins, on the other hand, was at home and treated me very cordially: courteous, calm and unassuming. He was too modest to try out the piano after I'd finished (though he apparently plays well. He requested a piano as his luxury item on *Desert Island Discs*. He didn't mention what kind, whereas Richard Ingrams – journalist and co-founder of *Private Eye* – stipulated a grand piano and, for his one book choice, *Teach Yourself Piano Tuning*). On the way out I couldn't help noticing the great black and white stills on his wall from *The Elephant Man* and more recent films. There's always an urge to pick their brains but I never do: the consummate professional. Not really, the dumbstruck tuner is nearer the mark for those early days.

Others were famous in certain circles. The clarinetist Jack Brymer, for example, was a household name among musicians and certain audiences. His name had been unknown to me at the time, but he was playing for top orchestras, and had appeared on television and done a lot of radio work too. It was only when I told a clarinetist friend of mine that I was tuning a piano for a bloke who plays the liquorice stick, you know, a clarinet, quite well-known apparently, that the friend, upon hearing the name Jack Brymer, gasped in reverential amazement and said he would have tuned the piano for nothing (though he couldn't tune pianos!). Fortunately, Brymer, like a lot of good musicians, wasn't of the elevated artiste type; he seemed quite laid back and very 'normal'. Being at the top of his profession (he used the piano mainly for his hobby of jazz), I asked him how many hours he practised a day. With a mock look of horror he answered, "Oh, I don't practise very often, it wears the reed out." I suspect there was an element of truth in this. I think he was able to go far on natural talent (rather like Russian pianist Horowitz, who said he rehearsed from time to time but never practised – an opposite view to one piano teacher who had a reminder on their wall: *You only need to practise on the days you eat*). It is known, similarly, that there have been certain sports heroes who, despite the advice from sports scientists and nutritionists, have still gained success despite being on the lazy side, eating the wrong food and not getting enough sleep (the names George Best and Rodney Marsh come to mind). Other top athletes and footballers will religiously do all the right things but still struggle to reach gold standard.

In my ignorance I tuned pianos for others who were well known in certain circles or were in the process of becoming household names. To those in the classical music world, the young composer Mark Anthony Turnidge was a rising star. To me he seemed like 'a young bloke' – most times he had an eleven o'clock shadow and spoke in a normal, rather non-descript accent. I always found him very easy to talk to. He didn't seem like my idea of 'a composer'. He lived in north London, and his composing room (well, it had a piano and large draughtsman-style board on a stand to accommodate his manuscript paper) overlooked the home of the Gunners football ground. I wished I'd asked him now, which was more important to him, Arsenal or (say) Shostakovich, for he was a rabid Gunners fan. I did once ask him where he did his composing (presumably he got away from the hubbub of London; no doubt he had favourite country haunts that inspired him to whisk his pen and paper out to record the local birdsong destined to be notated into a melodic flute line – minus the birdsong getting any copyright payments). I was surprised at his friendly scoff; he explained that he wasn't one of those composers who had to get away from it all in order to compose their masterpieces; he could compose almost anywhere (I guess against a backdrop of football chanting too – although if it was a home game, he'd be out and among them anyway).

Sir Laurens van der Post springs to mind also. Great soldier, traveller and writer, once a close friend and mentor of Prince Charles (I learned all this later). I sat in Mr Post's modest kitchen in Chelsea while he made us both a cup of tea. Although getting on, he still had a certain sartorial elegance, but he was unassuming and gave no hint of his many achievements. Over a cup of tea I asked this elderly gentleman whether he was retired, which opened the way to enquiring what line of business he had been in. He modestly said that he'd written a few travel books. For months later I always seemed to hear his name in the media or see it in print, and often associated with Prince Charles, yet hadn't heard of him previously.

The Winston family was another ordinary family who turned out to be not so ordinary. I mostly dealt with Mrs Winston, who'd inherited the Bechstein upright from her mother-in-law, who used to be a JP and mayoress of a north London borough. I'd tuned it for the elderly Mrs Winston over many years, also tuned the pianos at the Palmers Green day centre named in her honour. She was very fond of telling me about her son, who was a hard-working doctor. I hadn't met him at this point, not until the piano went to his household. He seemed a pretty down-to-earth chap on the few occasions we met at his home. Describing him as a doctor is a bit of an understatement as he shortly became a fertility specialist of national if not international repute, and later Lord Winston.

Though he may not be aware of it, Lord Winston's claim to fame is that he did the necessary and enabled my sister, via the lengthy NHS waiting system, to produce a son and heir. To my sister at the time he was merely a Hammersmith Hospital doctor who had managed, to use her technical vocabulary, to clear her tubes. She'd forgotten his name for some time, but after his rise to fame, strangely she could recall it with ease. According to her, he became the international fertility specialist who performed ground-breaking surgery on selected patients such as her.

The peculiar thing is that, perhaps because London is a small world, on two occasions I found myself tuning pianos for two other customers who owed having their off-spring to the work of Lord Winston. They didn't know each other, nor did they know that Lord Winston was one of my customers. It only came to light one day when I saw a special celebratory photograph taken of all 'Lord Winston's babies'. There was the great man, with distinctive moustache (not a health hazard?), there was my customer (with child) and there was another customer who, unknown to me, had benefited from the same treatment at Hammersmith Hospital. Meeting and watching my customer's young son grow up in six-monthly bites is a slightly strange experience. Had it not been for the decade we lived in, the choices offered to such couples, and the work of people like Lord Winston, that little smiling face, as yet unaware of the circumstances of how he came to be where he was, would not be enriching the many lives of those around him, day in, day out...

On the other hand, I did occasionally stare famous people in the face, though I wasn't necessarily there at their request. Tunings for concerts and shows come to mind, where it was common to bump into famous faces, though by the time I had realised who it was, they had usually disappeared. Tuning pianos situated in celebrities' London offices was regular Harrods work, too. Sir Harry Secombe comes to mind, though he was never in his London office while I was there tuning the piano. I began to take these hit-and-miss opportunities in my stride, however. Two other famous faces were Andrew Lloyd Webber and Richard Stilgoe; they were waiting for the lift as I made my way up to Mr Webber's (not then a Lord) office. Both were deep in conversation as I stepped out and they stepped in (it didn't seem an opportune moment to mention that my father was at the Royal College of Music around the same time as Mr Webber's father was teaching there – the organist and composer

William Lloyd Webber had come from fairly humble roots, I believe, his father being a self-employed plumber). I overheard no tantalising snippets about new projects from Messrs Webber and Stilgoe as we swopped places by the lift, but did get a brief hello and a nod as they disappeared discussing restaurants.

Rather bizarrely, I later found myself in the Kensington home of lyricist Don Black, a relatively unknown name to the general public but well known in show business (he wrote the lyrics to *Tell Me on a Sunday* and other established favourites of the masses). I was tuning his piano because his regular man, for whatever reason, was unable to do it. Don Black was working on an as yet unknown collaboration with Lloyd Webber: *Sunset Boulevard*. Black interrupted my tuning because he was wrestling over how the words would best fit the (new) tune sent to him. He couldn't play the piano (or at least couldn't read music) and, giving me the music, asked if I could give him an idea of how the melody line should go. I briefly felt I was part of another great West End collaboration, though how helpful I'd really been, I don't know.

On another occasion I was tuning a piano in a private residence in Chelsea when the sliding door to the room I was occupying was opened and Mr Bean, of all people, was standing there in the kitchen. Of course, it wasn't actually Mr Bean but the real Rowan Atkinson. He was taller than his screen image, and turned out to be collecting his girlfriend who was round at her mother's. I said a fleeting good morning; he nodded (rather shyly). Seconds passed... I wasn't in a sketch after all. He disappeared and I carried on.

Jim the under-foreman was never in awe of anyone (or pretended not to be). Presumably if it had been Frank Sinatra, Stanley Matthews or someone similar he might have shown a hint of enthusiasm. But there again the younger ones in the workshop wouldn't have been that interested in old man Sinatra, apart from a tinge of curiosity. I remember working away in the workshop once when Jim went to the showroom to bring a customer over. The customer hadn't seen much that he liked in the showroom and wanted to know what might be coming through soon from the workshop. He sauntered round lifting the lids of various pianos, trying them out here and there. We had a nice Ibach grand which eventually took his fancy. Ibach is a good make, though less well known than Steinway and others. People buying pianos often buy something (sadly like many other things now) merely because it is a big name. Whether a brand new Steinway or a second-hand one, some will still be below par (the 'Friday afternoon' piano, for example). Pianos must be bought on their individual merit. Many good manufacturers produced certain duff models or had periods in their long history when the quality was disappointing (even Steinways, and remember there is the German Steinway factory and the American one).

Much better to go purely on the touch, performance and tone of each individual piano, and sometimes lesser known but still respected makes such as Schiedmayer can prove to be real gems. However, it can all get quite confusing, with elements of trade secrecy or disputes being involved too, so the buyer is not always aware of what they are really buying. For example, in the 1980s the German Schiedmayer company ceased making pianos, but Ibach made some using the Schiedmayer name, then both the Japanese makers Kawai and UK firm Kemble also made some 'Schiedmayer' pianos (presumably some purchasers might have bought these feeling they were buying traditional German craftsmanship and quality). However, in time Kemble were owned by Yamaha pianos of Japan (and Kembles closed in 2009). Similarly, other British piano names such as Knight, Bentley and Welmar were at one time made under licence by one company. So, rather like buying a new British car, it's questionable just how

'British' some cars really are. As for pianos, just like a potential wife, looks can be deceiving: try her out first, changing models can be expensive, marry in haste… (Jim was prone to say).

The guy who Jim had brought over from the showroom was young, tallish, of slim build and with long curly hair (a descendant of Henry Purcell?); he seemed to be a cross between a hippy and a classical composer. Jim had to be polite but called him a long streak of piss after he'd gone (as he did anyone without a proper short back and sides). I have to confess I hadn't recognised him but some of the others were acting as though the Queen had just walked in. That's more accurate than it sounds, for it was Brian May from Freddie Mercury's pop band *Queen*. He was polite and patient, and knew what he wanted. Jim hadn't a clue who he was, other than he was 'one of those young types with too much money'.

So near yet so far, it seemed sometimes. By coincidence, a few years later I was tuning a piano for a client in Fulham, which I'd done for a number of years. On this occasion, the anonymous home on the opposite corner, seemingly done almost overnight, had lots of graffiti daubed on the walls and there were people hanging around either leaving flowers or reading the graffiti. I was told it was the home of Freddie Mercury, who had just died. Up to that point it had only been the local residents who were aware of who lived there, and that was largely because of the occasional loud parties, which the residents seemed to recognise was all par for the course when you have a rock star as a neighbour. The address, I was told, for a long time after became a shrine and had visitors from around the world who all knew exactly where to come.

I could be caught out. I'd recently enjoyed a highly popular series on television that was based on the true story of a women's POW camp. Some of the characters were likeable, others less so as they had prostituted themselves or turned informant. I particularly liked the nun. Despite such harsh conditions, both physical and mental, she was their saviour. Never giving up, always putting others before herself, tending the weak, showing compassion even for those who had chosen the wrong path. She was such a saintly and admirable character. I didn't know her real name so was caught by surprise when it was she who actually opened the door to her London home. It was difficult to conceal my delight after I clicked where I'd seen her but, trying to be professional (and rather shy anyway), I decided to avoid broaching the subject of films and acting. Alas, how disappointed I was with my 'nun'. With barely a hello, she pointed me in the direction of the piano and I never saw her again until I had to find her to say that I'd finished. With a signature on the card, it was a curt goodbye and that was it. She wasn't rude, exactly, but the illusion of compassion and humanity was definitely for the screen only. Rations of tea or coffee that morning, as in the internment camp of her 'past', had been distinctly absent.

Admittedly, it sometimes depended on whose piano it was. Perhaps she didn't play it. When partners are letting you in on behalf of someone else there can be a sense of you being a necessary evil, a chore. The clue is usually an opening remark such as, "How long do you think you'll be?" The quicker you're out the better, so they can turn the music up, finish the hoovering (or even may – who knows – carry on with their strip poker). In worst-case scenarios, the people don't even know that you need quiet to tune the piano. Screaming children, barking dogs, blaring radios, televisions that can't be turned off because it's someone's favourite programme; all have to be handled with careful negotiation. Alternatively, menacing looks and a hammer in your hand sometimes helps. Get the job done and move on quickly, for your sanity and theirs. Don't play peek-a-boo with the lovely three-year-old because she won't leave you alone, thinks you've come to entertain her for an hour. Don't stroke the cat because, the next thing, it's plonking up and down the keyboard trying to catch the felt mice that keep bobbing backwards and forwards inside.

North of the Thames, in salubrious Belgravia, I took on a new client through Harrods, Lord Armery. I was expecting a pompous man in the usual uniform: cravat, cuff links and suede shoes. He was at home, apparently, but the maid took care of me. Nothing unusual in that, but it's always slightly insulting when the owner can't bring themselves to come into the room and have a few words with the 'tradesman'. It was a nice enough grand, though a little dated. Rarely used, judging by the line of dust hidden inside (the dust silently falls, like a sprinkling of early winter frost, through the long hinge on the lid), and the undisturbed books and ornaments on top were not of an era I knew. When I had finished I was going to get the maid to sign the card, but she said, "I think sir will see you now." I felt like a boy entering the headmaster's study. I soon felt marginally embarrassed, however, as I was shown into a small bedroom and saw Lord Armery propped up in bed. Crisp pyjamas, redundant hot water bottle on the floor and a bedside cabinet full of pill bottles told their own story.

It turned out Lord A had turned ninety and rarely got out of bed before noon. The striped pyjamas did little to hide his thin, sagging body. "Now, how much do you want, old boy?" To the accompaniment of a wheezing chest, his shaky hands were grasping at ten-pound notes spewing from his wallet, which I attempted to catch before they fluttered to the floor. "It's okay, sir, you just have to sign the card. You have a contract."

"What? Oh, you sign it, will you." Rather bizarre, me signing it to say I'd been, but these cards were seldom seen by the office staff. His veiny hands with fossilised fingers seemed to be screaming out for *rigor mortis* to set in. He would have found it very challenging holding a pen. What surprised me more was that he then proceeded to get his diary out of his bedside cabinet and wanted to write in the next six-monthly appointment there and then.

I doubted his Lordship would be around next time but he was around for the next few years. I think his insistence on planning ahead helped to keep him going. I just found it strange because the piano was obviously not touched from one visit to the next. I'd been fussy the first time, not knowing who might emerge from what I thought was his Lordship's office. On subsequent visits I lost motivation, knowing the piano wasn't used. Also, it actually didn't require much attention. There is a myth that an unused piano will deteriorate badly, but the reverse is nearer the truth. Pianos that are played on frequently will go out of tune more quickly than unused ones. Consequently, I would have to sit there almost pretending to tune it. The fifteen or so minutes of work that it genuinely required would have appeared suspiciously short to the uninitiated, so I had to drag it out and found myself putting notes out of tune and then back in again (I couldn't charge him a smaller fee as the Harrods fee was set in stone).

To stimulate my brain a little I would cast my eye around the room as I worked. There were various fine paintings that had obviously once hung somewhere in the family's ancestral home – country estate out in the sticks. Silver-framed black-and-white photographs depicted his Lordship as a tall and dashing young man. He'd obviously led a racier life in the 1930s. Other bronze artwork and one or two quality hardback books containing soft lens shots of male nudes in a variety of positions helped to suggest why there had never been a Lady Armery. These shots, shown in magazines and elsewhere, might have been classified as pornographic, but sold and expensively packaged in hardback books as 'The Male Form', they could be classed as art. He was on his lonesome, apart from, that is, a weekly taxi ride to the

Garrick Club. He once got me to 'wire through and order some oysters'. I was glad to do so. They all knew him there, apparently. Pity I never got an invite – probably didn't have the right tie and flannels.

Towards the other end of the social scale, I still tuned non-Harrods customers as well, many of whom were getting on in years. One, a Mr Richards, had been a science teacher in an inner London secondary school. He didn't seem to have much to show for a lifetime in teaching: a tiny council flat. Crime in south London (notably lethal Lambeth) was notoriously high, with older people feeling particularly vulnerable.

I don't know how it came up in conversation, but Mr Richards was only too pleased to show any new visitor how secure his home was. All rooms had double locks on them. This seemed odd: to watch TV in the sitting room you had to find two appropriate keys. To get a drink at night you had apparently to use another two keys to get into the kitchen. "What d'you think of this then?" he asked proudly, waving a walking stick in front of me. I couldn't see an intruder being put off by an old man (sprightly though he was) with a walking stick. Before I could think of an encouraging reply he had me up against the fireplace with a six-inch blade millimetres from my chest. He was quick, no doubt about it. And it was only a demonstration: all over in seconds. It turned out that Mr R had also taught fencing for many years. His 'stick', one of several placed about the flat in strategic positions, disguised a lethal weapon which revealed itself at the end of the stick after pressing a button in the handle. Quite effective in his hands, as it would have been difficult to get anywhere near him when he was lunging in what he had just demonstrated to me as (presumably) the en garde or attack position. The glinting blade attached to the end of a wooden rod was, thankfully, soon put carefully away. There was no 'They don't like it up 'em' foolery here. Pity the poor blighter who chooses to burgle this house. Sad thing was, it wasn't a house, just a drab flat with nothing to steal, containing an elderly man keeping vigil over wife and memories, waiting for the inevitable.

Mrs Beetle had done better for herself. She was a tiny lady who really was aged ninety-eight. Her name wasn't really Beetle, but that's the creature I associated her with in my mind. Tiny steps, rounded back, little grey head with limited side movement; it would take her an eternity to cross the living-room floor. No stick needed, she could scuttle but it required a lot of steam for the minimum of progress. It's quite something to be in the presence of someone who has lived for nearly a century – or at least someone who is still very able-minded if not totally able-bodied.

The first time I visited Mrs Beetle I thought it would be the usual: the piano was a good-sized grand, but it was an ornament, not played from one year to the next. I was expecting the daughter to be there, as she'd made the appointment over the phone, but no, Mrs Beetle was very independent. She lived in Catford, alone now, but it was a well-kept home with a trim garden front and back. The furniture and decor, although all well cared for, were like museum pieces; in fact, it was a better 1940s house than the kind of examples exhibited in the Imperial War Museum and elsewhere. Even all the plugs and sockets were of the ancient, round pin variety. I'd wanted to get the hoover from my car to remove a carpet of dust from under the keyboard, but modern appliances couldn't be used in this house. Instead, she dragged out an ancient gold and black contraption that looked as though it ran on coal. It coughed and spluttered, struggling to suck more than two stray hairs at a time as I manoeuvred it along. In no time at all it had spat out the said hairs along with an inch of dust. I feared the neighbours might be put off by this orchestra of screaming bagpipes so put the 'award-winning' dust extractor away, thanking Mrs B for the tray of tea which I could see being wheeled (wisely) in on a hostess trolley. This was real tea, evidence being: tea pot, cosy, extra hot water, tea strainer for the tea leaves, milk in a small jug. I could tell by the array of music that, in fact, although the piano hadn't been maintained regularly of late, it was no ornament. The sheet music and scores were well-thumbed; Mrs B wasn't going to offload them onto me.

Only once would I make the mistake of accepting an elderly customer's cabinet of tattered music. She had taken my hesitation as a yes and gleefully helped to load up my car with the yellow and battered remnants of number-one hits from the 1910s. It was under the guise of doing me a favour; she was sure that I would love to play them or, in my line of work, would find a good home for them. "No. Before you offer, I won't accept a penny for them. Not a penny!" For days they were driven around in the boot of my car, with stacks more across the backseat, sapping the petrol from my tank. I couldn't give them away. "Worthless," dealers told me politely before showing me hundreds of the same. That shrewd lady had got her room cleared and saved herself a trip to the council refuse depot.

It turned out that Mrs Beetle had only stopped teaching two years ago but she still liked to keep her hand in occasionally. After I finished the tuning, although expecting her to decline the offer, out of politeness more than anything, I invited her to play. It took a good ten minutes before she arrived at the piano and attempted to inch the old stool into the correct position. Being jam-packed with Brahms, Liszt and Mozart piano classics, it took every ounce of her strength. She climbed up onto the stool as though she was one of those early Victorian female mountaineers. I was beginning to clock-watch, knowing another customer would be waiting in for me. Only when she was comfortable would Mrs B begin. A tinge of guilt soon pinched my restless thoughts. Boy could she play! Put a fish in the right water and nature's harmony is as one: faultless, beautiful from all angles, breath-taking in its simplicity, awesome in its very being. Mrs B's fingers rattled up and down the keyboard as though she were not a ninety-year-old but a nine-year-old prodigy.

Age, arthritis, worn-out tendons, delays or hold-ups in synaptic pathways, none of these could be detected in the sonorous sounds that wafted around the room. She seemed sheepish and apologised for 'a few wrong notes' (though I'm pretty sure there hadn't been any), and was complimentary about the tuning. I put the tea things in the kitchen. She washed, I dried and then I bade her goodbye, already looking forward to future visits.

Mrs B's playing was such a contrast to that of some of my other customers. Why did Mr Williams, for example, always start with the same conversation after I had finished the tuning? "I don't really play, but…" It was as if he was saying, "Oh, all right, if you insist…" Fair enough, he could rattle off passages from a few famous classics he dimly remembered from his boyhood lessons (the scars on the knuckles had long since healed), but did he not know that he always stumbled in exactly the same place whenever he got round to playing Bach's Fugue and Toccata (colloquially known as 'fudge and tomato')? I suppose I should have felt grateful, as his drying up became his own signal (excluding one or two further unsuccessful attempts to get past the same tricky bars) for him to stop. Surely he must have remembered that he fluffed that passage last time? Seemingly not. "Oh, dear, I rather bungled that bit… I'll have to practise that for your next visit. Never mind. It's time I settled up, isn't it?" He had the unusual occupation of being a Toastmaster, a sort of professional Master of Ceremonies, and could occasionally be seen in the media when compèring or introducing famous people at big charity events. He was meticulous in his dress and manner but less so when playing rather too demanding piano pieces.

Unfortunately, unbeknown to some of them, a few of my customers often displayed all manner of grimaces and twitches whilst they played. A few were competent pianists who could produce exquisite sounds, some fared less favourably, but it is difficult to pay attention to the music when the performer looks as though they are about to have some sort of seizure when they are engrossed in their performance. I learnt quickly that one has to be careful not to smile, let alone laugh, as these pianists, apparently deep in concentration, are prone at any moment to snatch a glance at you to see if you are enjoying the performance as much as they are.

By the time I'd come across one particularly skilled 'Mr Grimace', I'd learnt that the trick is either to close one's eyes or else try and vacuum-pack one's tongue and mouth in the closed position. Then I could watch, with fascination, as Mr Grimace sat perched on his piano stool. His posture was good, no tension in the shoulders, though he was prone to some erratic rocking and movement of the head. His performance, neck up, seen from the side, revealed a drooling tongue, and the shiver of alternating current that darted back and forth from one eyebrow to the other, as though a surgeon's needle was pulling up the end of a stitch. Less pleasant (though peculiarly fascinating, partly because Mr Grimace seemed unaware of his bodily functions) was the occasional sight of spittle dropping onto the keys as he played rather difficult Mozart pieces. Maybe it lubricated his fingers whilst he played, although between sonatas he would reach for his green-stained handkerchief and wipe the keys over in a perfunctory manner. This was the same loyal hanky used to wipe the mouthpiece of his telephone, or hold the bakelite handle of the saucepan heating milk for my coffee. I always brought a clean cloth and my own Mr Sheen to Mr Grimace's abode and made sure I gave the keyboard a good wipe before I started to tune the piano. He thought I was marvellously efficient.

Alas, I was less efficient if Mr Grimace or other of my customers with a similar disposition to pull faces, asked me to turn pages as they soldiered on. Turning at the right moment was exceedingly difficult when some of them gave very indistinct cues. I knew when we were coming to the last few bars on a given page, of course, but the pianist's cue to turn the page – usually a nod or some physical clue – was practically impossible to decipher if they had been bouncing around, nodding and grimacing throughout most of the piece. Often was the time, in the heat of an exciting moment and not wanting to let the performer down, I turned too early, giving rise to a sort of premature ejaculation feeling (I would imagine!). The likes of Mr Grimace could recover by snatching a page back (alas sometimes tearing it clean down the middle), but I always felt it was me who had spoilt the performance.

Mr Grimace's neighbour, three doors down, seemed to live in a time warp (actually, Mr Grimace did not know this neighbour, Mr Vaughan; none of his neighbours really knew much about him). It was a large detached house. Through the glass window of his garage door I could see that Mr Vaughan had a Triumph Herald tucked away in the garage, but he said he never used it as 'the tax has run out'. It had run out two decades ago. I could work out from the captioned photographs of Mr Vaughan as an attractive, blond county schoolboy cricketer that he was, in fact, only just into his sixties, though he looked nearer seventy-five. Only a few wisps of hair were left, his chin had been shaved in the conventional way, but the shadowy bits just under the ears and close to the jawbone, had been, like his garden, neglected. His back and shoulders were as rounded as the Arc de Triomphe. On the other hand, his hearing and mental faculties seemed to be as sharp as ever.

His home had obviously not been dusted since his mother had passed on, nor decorated (and the smell of moth balls hit anyone as soon as they entered the front door). He had money and time, having taken early retirement from a City bank, but the clock had stopped. He only played the piano ('Fur Elise' and other schoolboy pieces) and had it tuned because it was more his mother's piano than his and, "She wouldn't like to see it go to rack and ruin, now that she is no longer with us." The frizzled carpets had pages from *The Daily Telegraph* to cover the worst of the gaping holes. Window frames were rotten and draughty; the paint on the ceiling was flaking away, frustrating a resident spider who was having to constantly rebuild its home. Around the house, flat surfaces all appeared to be taken up with piles of selected cuttings from newspapers (even on the windowsill in the bathroom). I couldn't resist furtive looks, wondering if there would be a collection of unsolved murder reports.

But Mr Vaughan was no murderer, hardly went out; his two chosen subjects were cricket and Princess Diana. I should have guessed the cricket as, unfailingly, if it was the right season, he'd always have the cricket on the radio or TV when I visited. He obviously also had a fond liking for Diana as, in addition to the copious Diana press cuttings, there was a framed photograph of her in prime position on the mantelpiece in the sitting room. And yes, it stood out because, unlike everything else, it was obviously dusted and shined every day.

He was a nice enough chap was Mr Vaughan. Quiet and slow, but probably thought he was pretty normal. He had his copy of the *Radio Times*, a regular feature in most homes belonging to people of his class and generation; it had the familiar circles drawn around the evening's viewing, up to the day of my visit. On the outside of the home, the overgrown front garden and smoky net curtains, behind which could be seen stark light bulbs with no lamp shades, probably hinted at unusualness to passers-by, but the back garden was a war he'd obviously lost a long time ago. The strimmer rested against the French windows in the living room (actually *in* the living room). Bits of ancient grass emanated from its underneath. On my first visit I had thought it was resting there on the living-room carpet (or remnants of), with him waiting for me to finish the tuning before he could set about the garden. "You've got your hands full there," I had joked, looking at the garden, and he'd smiled back. But that strimmer was always there. It never moved, though on each visit the garden came closer and closer to the French windows and began to send the house into semi-darkness.

Unfortunately, he was good enough to make me a drink. He was from the old school: you don't ask, it goes without saying that the host will make a drink for the visitor. There were numerous used tea and coffee cups around the house, some with excellent penicillin cultures, so the trick was to play the helpful guest in appreciation of the hospitable host. Having pretended to take sips of coffee from the gravelly concoction, laced with evaporated milk, '...now that the milkman no longer delivers', I would time my sneak out to the kitchen with a roar of the crowd applauding a good run or catch on the television. "Howzat!" I could have shouted as I swiftly poured the concoction down the sink (always remembering to run the tap and wash away the evidence that showed a whole cup had been discharged). Hopefully, he saw this act of washing-up as my being very civil. By this time I was experienced enough not to tip it into the nearest plant pot. I'd done that once in another customer's house: having valiantly consumed half a cup of what tasted vaguely like tea-flavoured hot milk, the rest was used to surreptitiously water/milk a plant. To my horror, the tea drained straight through the pot and nearly flooded an expensive stereo speaker on top of which the plant pot was resting. The owner eyed me suspiciously but said nothing.

This plan A (deploying pot plants) had been a failure; plan B, practised with the likes of Mr Vaughan, worked if I could slip into the kitchen very swiftly. Plan C is to merely apologise and say, disappointingly, "How silly! I forgot all about it and now it's gone cold. Terribly sorry." This works well provided the host is not too insistent on making you a fresh cup. It may be, with some of them, that they have their own motives for making undrinkable drinks. It's not that they want to poison you (unless, I suppose, they offer you a drink *after* you have completed the tuning), but they figure that if they make you such an appalling cup, you will never accept such an offer again and they won't be saddled with that particular domestic chore.

At least Mr Vaughan didn't ask me to do tasks people of his mother's generation occasionally did. Apparently, it had once been within the remit of pre-war tuners to – on top of the tuning – not only clean out the piano and distribute camphor inside to ward off the moths, but adjust or mend radiograms, and replace broken turntable rubber bands. If these tuners were representing music stores, then the selling of sheet music was also a duty. At least I had modern transport to get around on. The father of the great English composer, Sir Edward Elgar, was a piano tuner from a much earlier era. Clutching a leather bag and with top hat in place, he apparently used to get around to his customers in outlying districts of Worcester on horseback.

For a time I owned an ex-NHS Bedford ambulance – not the smoothest thing to arrive in when attending parties or family weddings – but when I had aspirations for doing a bit of buying and selling of pianos, it was a necessity as well as a novelty. My piano-dealing days were short-lived, however, as the muscle needed to move pianos around was one of numerous problems I hadn't fully taken into consideration.

The ambulance, a pacey automatic, was fun to drive around in (though extremely thirsty). There were no flashing lights on it but, when on the road, people still seemed to give way and let

---

Albert E. Blamey,
Tuner to Sir Edward Elgar, Royal Academy
of Music,
EXPERT PIANO TUNER,
15 Years' West End Experience,
FINE TUNINGS & PLAYER PIANO
WORK A SPECIALITY, TERMS MODERATE,
14, Fairholme Road, Harrow

Above: a bit of Elgar name-dropping doesn't go amiss in this 1920 London newspaper advert. No sign of a number for the fairly newfangled telephone, so the practice of sending a card requesting an appointment must have still been in vogue.

me in everywhere. Heads were turned one day, however, when I'd agreed to buy an upright piano off one customer. They'd merely wanted rid of said piano, so practically gave it away on condition I took it by the end of the week. I don't know why, but this particular piano was an awkward size and had toes (its feet at each end) that were longer than usual: I had the ambulance on the icy pavement and, with a friend helping, wiggle and swivel as we might, I could not get the piano in to the back of the ambulance (partly because it still had the seats down each side); there it rested, on the top step of the ambulance's rear steps. It was not the steep incline that was the problem; the ambulance's doors were a fraction too narrow. I had to beg for a large saw so that I could do a part-amputation of the toes. As always, passers-by couldn't help giving funny looks or funny comments ("You name it, son, I'll play it… ha, ha"); worse still were those who decided to plink and plonk on it whilst I was bent double, sweating away trying to saw the ends but, at the same time, look cool calm and collected (difficult when I was very concerned that the piano was about to jump off the ambulance step and bounce down the hill).

Adjusting clocks, changing record styluses, re-hanging pictures, repairing wheezing harmoniums, too, were all things that a few old customers expected 'good' tuners to be able to handle. Such jobs were sometimes a can of worms, as the object being repaired invariably fell to bits. An Oscar-winning performance on the part of the customer, heart-broken that you had 'destroyed' something that had been in the family for years, invariably left me well out of pocket.

A few customers were incredulous that I could make a living just tuning pianos. If the "Don't you do anything else?" remark got too wearing I would respond, as straight-faced as possible, "I get by... though I do do a bit of chimney sweeping in the winter, just to help make ends meet."

My problem with customer relations in my younger days was my shyness. Why did I always have to say yes when I knew, from past visits, that the forthcoming tea was going to be an unnecessary punishment? Why could I never put my fees up when, after five years of loyal service, a modest increase would have been perfectly reasonable? Some customers I would have dearly liked to drop: they were too far away, too rude or rarely in when they said they would be. The problem was, early on, beggars can't be choosers. I needed their custom, and I was a coward anyway. Additionally, with Harrods customers, once having agreed to take them on, I couldn't really drop them. And so it was with Miss Steiner.

She had plenty of money tied up in property in Germany, but lived a fairly frugal existence in a London suburb. Miss Steiner shared her modest detached home with her live-in companion, George. Apart from her obsession with gardening, George came first in everything. Of French extraction, George had to have the best meals, plenty to drink and all the home comforts.

Sitting on the best chair, you would think that George would have appreciated the lady of the house carefully brushing his hair, but no, he would snap and growl as Miss Steiner forced the brush through his stubborn coat. I've never found poodles the friendliest of animals, though I can imagine what it's like to have your hair tugged the wrong way and then be forced to parade past the neighbours in a pink bow. What was excruciatingly annoying and embarrassing was the fact that George would lock on to my leg the moment I entered the house. No amount of, "Down, boy," or violent shaking of the leg would elicit a dismount (indeed, it seemed to add to his pleasure). What made it worse was the fact that Miss Steiner carried on as though everything was perfectly normal. She pretended that she could not see her dear Georgie ruining a good pair of trousers, or that her piano tuner was walking with a severe limp. We had to talk about the weather, the traffic and the piano while, below, loveable Georgie made up for six years without a female canine companion.

I used to dread these visits, and, being braver on the phone, had meekly intimated that it might be a good idea to keep George in the other room while I was tuning the piano, as the barking was a distraction. But such agreements proved to only ever be temporary; they were soon forgotten once Miss Steiner saw how keen George was to see me. With the tuning over, she now deemed it okay to let Georgie back into the living room (unfortunately considered 'his' room), resulting in a very delayed exit for me. Finally, though, old age got the better of that poodle and he slipped away not a day too soon. It seemed a great burden had been lifted from my shoulders (and leg).

It's strange the precious things people keep hidden away. When she knew me better, Miss Steiner once got a fragile and dusty box out. In it were two train tickets which meant a lot to her. Although she was not actually Jewish herself (at least that's what she always stipulated), she explained that, as a little girl living in Germany, her father had been taken away, and she and her mother had been told to get out of Germany as quickly as they could. These tickets had been for the very last available train to free her from Germany. That's how she came to be living in London. Her mother looked after her until she grew up, but she never saw her father again.

Having mentioned 'slipping away' earlier, I went through an alarming period of having quite a few customers slip away. In the normal run of things this would have appeared pretty normal, as they were invariably not in their prime of life. However, there did seem to be an unnerving correlation between the piece of music I had recently learned to play in order to try out the piano after tuning it, and the subsequent demise of my clientele. Old people die but I felt they shouldn't be doing so to the extent that they were dropping off at a faster rate than I was able to replace them with new customers.

When it came to playing the piano after tuning it, I was good at bluffing my way. I don't mean like one of the Harrods salesmen in the showroom, who was adept at discreetly picking up keys that shouldn't have been sticking down as he demonstrated in arpeggioic form a reconditioned piano. He knew what pianos to let rip on and what were better suited to a more graceful, legato approach. No, invariably I would play opening bars from well-known sonatas, giving a fairly accomplished performance before stopping or leading into another masterpiece (of which I only really knew the first page or so). If I heard the owner enter the room I would pretend to have been caught by surprise and stop abruptly. "Oh, do carry on, that was beautiful," would be the usual enthusiastic response from a non-musician. But I'd feign modesty and an urgency to get on to my next customer. In reality I could never finish a sonata, having only learnt a few pages from one of the 'favourites' (avoiding the difficult bits), but I think it made the piano sound quite impressive and gave the illusion that I was quite an accomplished pianist with a good repertoire.

Only occasionally was I caught out when little eight-year-old Sebastian or Henrietta would step into the limelight (or were pushed – even if it was their piano) and proceed to play the whole sonata I had just attempted to play, note-perfect and at the correct tempo. Do precocious children know they are precocious? (Or would that merely confirm their precociousness?) It certainly put me on my guard regarding tuning the piano properly. You could never be entirely sure if the child pianist (sometimes hidden away upstairs doing their homework) was a raw beginner or a distant relation of Mozart's. I have, on occasions, taken painstaking care in tuning a piano because the parents have spoken in such a glowing way about their 'gifted' child. They deserved the best that money could buy. What a disappointment when the said child proves to show great difficulty in locating middle C, and can barely manage one finger at a time, prodding the eight white notes of C major, or even bashing out 'Twinkle, Twinkle Little Star', but unable to venture any further. As the proud parents look on, I too give an encouraging clap whilst fighting to hide my disappointment and attack of yawning.

Returning to the slipping away of certain customers, I'd developed the penchant for playing quite a few bars of the slow movement of Chopin's 'Marche funèbre' (the Funeral March). Despite its title and deathly associations, the second movement has a lovely melody that is also quite a good test of the piano's tuning and action (being the slow movement it was more within my capabilities too). Unfortunately, it seemed to be more than mere coincidence that, after playing this piece, the customer would not survive long enough for me to visit them again when the next tuning was due. I put it down to coincidence to begin with but it seemed to occur too frequently. 'Marche funèbre' became a curse and, after four unrelated customers had passed on during the gap between my last and forthcoming visit, I started to explore tunes with a more optimistic note to use as my party piece ('Always Look on the Bright Side of Life', perhaps?).

On the first occasion, I had made the mistake of simply turning up at the time agreed after the last appointment. She was a reliable old soul, was Miss Turner (no relation to me), so I just came along at the usual time, having not heard anything to the contrary after sending a Harrods reminder postcard. I decided I would visit as normal and she would send a cheque off to Mr Al-Fayed in the Brompton Road. I knew the Kensington flat well, every room, every precious ornament. Each Christmas I couldn't help keeping a lookout for the personal Christmas card sent to her ('aunty') from Prince Charles. It was strange, at first, to see one among numerous cards that happened to be from the (possibly) future king.

I suppose I had got marginally closer than this to the royal family through tuning the piano of one of the Queen's Ladies-in-Waiting (a euphemism for personal servant or wannabe Queen). Her husband was the man who was involved with the BBC for a time, with the ridiculous name of Marmaduke Hussey. With a name like that it's surprising he made a success of anything (why does it remind one of a lolloping Great Dane?). At least Lady Hussey was good enough to make me a cup of tea (actually, it's quite nice to have a Lady-in-Waiting). My claim to fame is that I was offered and ate a slice of royal cake left over from Charles and Diana's wedding (I heroically avoided saying 'Chas and Di' to the Lady herself). It had found its way to my upper intestines via the dutiful Lady's hostess trolley. I can't say that it tasted any better than a Sainsbury's fruit cake, but it didn't stop me saying I had royal connections.

I already had business cards printed, and despite Harrods still having their royal warrant at that time, I refrained from having *by royal appointment* on my cards. In this instance you can't have your cake and eat it, so references to royalty were not added after the wedding cake contribution. I also managed to avoid the puns and clichés when having my business card designed: '*A sound service*'... '*Highly strung*', etc. (better than one undertaker who included *Yours eventually* on his business card).

Getting back to my namesake, Miss Turner, I was a little peeved that she was slower than normal in answering the door. I knew her to be somewhat hard of hearing, so I knocked louder (I, like those from the criminal fraternity, merely had to push the tradesman button to gain access into the building). The loud knock brought an unknown neighbour to his door. "I'm trying to get hold of Miss Turner." He replied that she no longer lived there. I felt really put out as she might at least have had the courtesy to let me know of a change of address. "Can I get in touch with her?" I enquired, to which he answered rather dryly, "Only through a medium, I would imagine. She died two months ago."

Similar roundabout messages came into play following other customers where I'd played my snippet of 'Marche funèbre'; I just couldn't afford to test my theory any further. Of course, if at all possible, I preferred the customer to do the playing: I tended to freeze if an audience built up whilst I was playing. Even in the case of Mrs Munro over in Hillingdon, her playing was preferable to mine. The husband was a retired doctor and part of the small minority who can't stand the sound of a piano being tuned. (The dribbling ladies in the old folks' home are the same. They think I can't hear them swearing and moaning when I disturb their peace in the morning by tuning the piano cooked by their severe central heating system. I have them eating out of my hands when I finish an hour later with such hits as 'Roll Me Over in the Clover' or 'Pack Up Your Troubles'. It's nice to see them all come alive and shout out requests. I nearly always leave with a round of applause and comments such as 'Lovely man' or 'Are you coming tomorrow, dear?' The earlier 'What a racket!', 'Can't someone shut that dreadful man up?' comments have been long forgotten. I used to quite like these visits as the old folk were not very discriminating about good and poor playing. The matron in charge seemed nice enough, though a little strange. I once asked her about May, usually a regular in the horse-shoe of crumpled bodies in the living-room but missing on that day. "Oh, she's fine," matron responded. I chipped in positively, "Good. She's in her room, is she?" Matron wasn't expecting a follow-up question and left me briskly with: "Er, no. She died… last Wednesday, I think." I noticed a few years after I'd moved on from tuning at the home that they and the matron were at the centre of a scandal involving mismanagement.

Mrs Munro's husband, the retired doctor, I never met, as he always chose to visit the library on the mornings of my visits to tune her upright. I believe he too, like his wife, was Scottish, though he apparently thought little of his wife's playing and offered her no encouragement. I found that she could play quite well (among her repertoire of Liszt and Chopin were old poppy or musical ballads such as 'Memories' from *Cats*), but had a very spidery kind of style. With wispy hair and spindly stair-rod arms and legs, her feet hardly had strength enough to push the pedals down. Likewise with her dainty fingers. She'd play most of the right notes but any haunting melody would be reduced to a fleeting, staccato interpretation. In her bid to maintain what she considered to be the right tempo (in reality, everything was played like a Scottish jig), many a good tune came over as a whispered version with occasional notes missing due to her not exerting sufficient pressure on certain of the keys. A sound like clicking knitting needles could be heard as her fingernails spun a web of quavers up and down the piano.

She was always fascinated by the large coffee jar of water we kept in the bottom of the piano to help prevent it from drying out. Had she not heard of evaporation? On every visit it was, "Ooh, look. Marvellous, it's all gone." The replenishing of the glass jar with fresh water became something of a ritual. Retrieving it from its dusty hole in a dark corner of the piano's bottom compartment, I had to hold it up for her inspection. It would be carefully filled up as if she were providing running clean water for starving Africans. Wiping the jar with a tea towel, she would ceremoniously hand it back to me: "There you are, Mr Turner... amazing... Hopefully that will last until your next visit." I don't think the piano was likely to die even if the water did completely evaporate.

Mrs Munro's face would light up as soon as she saw me climbing out of the car. She knew we had something in common – a love of music – even if her husband didn't. Invariably she would tell me of her last holiday, which was usually a cruise or flight out to Italy, but the two weeks spent in a plush British hotel later in the year – every year – would also be faithfully reported on. In particular, an account and description of the resident pianist who played in the lounge bar or hotel restaurant was always given (why did she seem surprised that I didn't know the Eastbourne piano or its pianist personally?).

On one of my earliest visits I'd initially found her topic of conversation rather embarrassing. She insisted on talking about the wonderful penis she had seen on holiday. I didn't know if this was her peculiar sense of humour or perhaps something to do with her husband's line of work until I realised that, "I couldn't help staring at the marvellous penis" (all said completely straight faced) was, after translation from her heavy accent, something about the new pianist. I had been on the verge of either bursting out laughing or walking out of the room in disgust. On subsequent visits, when she got on to her favourite subject of penises, I more or less knew the long and short of it by then.

Over in Battersea I had an audience of one, and hadn't even realised for quite a while that anyone was there. I was making daily trips to a church in order to partly overhaul an old grand piano. It was about a week's work, and I'd been given my own key to let myself in. An incredibly quaint little church, nestling next to the Thames, it was hidden away in a backwater behind numerous council and private tower blocks. The artist, Turner (great name!), apparently, had used it as a site for painting a view across the Thames.

One day I was in the empty church, fully engrossed in my work when I heard a voice say, "I shouldn't do that." It came not from above but from a man sitting in a pew some rows back. It was the sort of comment to get my back up, the sort said when you're working on a piano in a pub and a late-afternoon punter is determined to strike up a conversation. They usually tell you 'interesting' facts, such as that all piano tuners are blind or that their aunty was the best piano player in Bermondsey, could play anything, once won Pub Pianist of the Year (1906 or 1966?), didn't need no moozic… played by ear as well as with her hands, ha, ha… You must 'ave 'eard of Ruby Godsall, surely? Nearly appeared on *Opportunity Knocks* once…

To the voice in the church I wanted to say, "How can I repair it if I'm not allowed to touch it?" but thought it better to pretend I hadn't heard anything. Maybe he'd go away. "No, no. I mean *I* shouldn't touch it. Very skilled job, that!" He must have read my thoughts. As the piano looked in a sorry state, almost disembowelled with all the strings off, I began to suspect that he initially might have thought I was vandalising it. I didn't have time to stop work so I carried on a bitty conversation with me working and him still sitting several rows back. The conversation warmed after he twigged that I was there for legitimate reasons and it dawned on me that he had much less right to be there than me (I'd been given a set of keys and should have locked myself in). He wouldn't come over so I eventually walked a couple of rows up and worked away with some small piano bits in my hand as we chatted. Scrawny, unshaven and with a peculiar 'pic 'n' mix' set of clothes that were enveloped in an old, stained raincoat two or three sizes too big for him, I realised he was a tramp who had taken advantage of the open door. In fact, he knew the church, or at least the vicar, who was no doubt in his book of ticks and crosses. The vicar was out and I was worried he might get difficult when I wanted to lock up, but I needn't have worried. He was quite meek and obliging.

In the course of the afternoon I'd heard how he'd come to be trudging the streets of London. I can't verify whether it was true or not, but his story centred on his marriage of five or six years past. He'd been happily married and had been a successful economist. That is until he'd tragically knocked down and killed his beautiful daughter in his own car. From that day on he could never live with what he had done; he found it impossible to be in the same house as his wife and said he would never ever accept her forgiveness, though it had been repeatedly offered.

Drink had reared its ugly head (though I did half wonder if drink had played a part in the accident) and he'd started the slippery slope of losing his job, home and wife. He was perfectly coherent with me and obviously not on drink now. There seemed to remain a vestige of pride; at no point did he ask me for money or anything else. By five o' clock, curious, I asked him where he was going now that the church had to be locked and the vicar wasn't at home (I knew he was on holiday). "I'm going to another church," he said, almost secretively. Upon hearing that it was the relatively well-known St. John's in Smith Square, I offered to take him as it was raining and St. John's wasn't far out of my way. Once he was in the car, the reason he'd sat three rows back became abundantly clear. I kind of admired him for that, now knowing that his overpowering odour was why he had wanted to keep his distance.

We passed a chip shop not long after we had got started so I stopped and bought him a bag of chips. He was embarrassed but grateful. I wondered what was so special about St. John's. He told me he'd hidden his things there and, secondly, he knew a good place round the back for sleeping at night. He hesitated momentarily before saying more, but then revealed that he knew just where the external warm-air vent from the heating system was located. He also said bakeries were another good option, as they have warm walls in the early mornings. When we arrived he took the remainder of his chips and disappeared round the back just as some early concert-goers, a few with bow ties sprouting out of the tops of their smart rain coats, hurried up the front steps and out of the cold. How strange, I thought, that we get uptight about such things as time and appearance, whereas others in society are far less concerned about appearance or even what day it is.

Perhaps I should admit here to being rather small-minded. The first time I visited Mr Stagg he had complained about my being late. Ten minutes' lateness would be nothing to another customer (who would be 'in all morning – come when you're ready'), but some were obsessive about punctuality. Trouble is, I've generally found that you can't be more than just a few minutes early. Ten minutes early seems to fluster some people as much as others disliking you being five minutes late. Mr Stagg wasn't one of those who have a house full of clocks like one or two of my other customers did. In one, against the annoying background of ticking grandfather and carriage clocks, you'd wait for one set of chimes to stop only to hear another set kick off (or the cursed cuckoo clock). Retired, he seemed to spend much of his spare time tinkering with clocks.

The ones in his main rooms would all be slightly out of sync, and made their 'best' racket at eleven o'clock or midday (far better to have one o'clock appointments for these horological horrors: even today I have nightmares about the infernal ticking of clocks!).

No, after his disgruntled moan over my tardiness delaying his wife's late morning plans, I made up my mind that if Mr Stagg was so concerned with the time, I'd never be late again (he had calmed down as my tuning neared completion, but I think he also felt slightly embarrassed at having left a disgruntled message on my answerphone – he told me to ignore it when I got home, because I was here now, at last).

Arriving home at the end of the day I was greeted with his clipped answerphone message (decipherable after I heard the second attempt). Like a lot of my older customers, when answerphones were the latest technology (no such things as mobile phones then, and this new-fangled answerphone technology was nothing more than a rather cumbersome tape-cassette/recorder-style machine connected to the landline), he and they were flummoxed to start with. After hearing my initial recorded message they would wait for the 'real' voice to come on: "Hello... hello... are you there, Mr Turner?" Hearing nothing, they would hang up and immediately try again. Still I wasn't there. They hadn't got the gist of the idea that it was a machine that couldn't turn back into a thinking human. My grandmother had a similar misconception when she was first given a cine camera: her early films made you quite seasick. The method in her madness was the fact that it was a 'movie' camera, so tended to wave it around quite a bit.

With the answerphone, two other problems arose for new users. Some customers would not wait until the tone (or 'beep'); thinking it might cut them off or that they had to get their message in *before* the beep, they spoke as soon as they heard my recorded message. Anything these customers said before the beep had sounded would not be recorded on the machine. Many a time I heard only the frustrating tail end of a message, caught as they finished their message after the beep – in the place where they were supposed to leave their full message: "…Bye now. Look forward to seeing you at ten o'clock." Who the hell was it? (My ESP wasn't that reliable, and why did so many forget to leave their telephone number?) An alternative habit for first-time users was, after hearing the cue 'Please speak after the tone', to simply freeze. I can almost see him now, Mr Stagg, a stag caught in the headlights. But the likes of some of the Stagg generation mastered the technology quite quickly and chose to use it as a sounding board and emotional crutch. On and on they went, using up my tape space, taking twenty minutes to say they were having new flock wallpaper in the lounge so would I not call in February, weather might be better in March anyway, but the decorator might not have finished by then, but hopefully he would have done, very reliable is Mr Jones, never let them down before… By the way…

Other callers had adapted more quickly to the answerphone and, annoyingly, chose not to leave a message at all. In those days, with no dial back or similar technology available, all I heard was a beep and a long moment of silence until the caller had put the receiver down (or slammed it down). It always left me wondering, who was it? It could have been the BBC, the Queen, surely it's not too much to ask that they leave a message? (Only *I* was allowed to hang up whenever I heard an answerphone machine; personally I couldn't stand them.) But some of these callers seemed unaware that anything they said would be picked up in the time after the beep and their replacing the receiver. I often caught snatches from erstwhile sober and polite customers: "Damn," or: "It's one of those bloody machines, Beth," or (shouting at the machine): "Why is he *never* at home, confounded man."

Mr Stagg's virginal recorded message wasn't in the 'disgusted of Tunbridge Wells' league, but the point was taken: I was eight minutes late, was I coming or not?

It was a horrible journey, right across London. I'd no other customers in the area, should have given the Staggs up, really, but the retired Mr Stagg wouldn't have anyone else. He perhaps saw in me, a young man, someone who would see him and the piano out. Not that it was an old piano, quite a valuable Bechstein upright, actually (and I'd originally been sent by Harrods to replace a dud bass string). He never touched it and, as they'd never had any children, I suppose the piano was 'their baby', or at least his wife's. He worshipped his wife and she worshipped the piano. Or had done so some decades ago. It sounds harsh but I grew to despise her. She looked the spitting image of *Coronation Street*'s one-time Ena Sharples, even had the hairnet.

Sometime during the tuning, Ena Sharples would summon the strength to climb into the electric stair-lift and glide down to the front room to regale me about her various illnesses – how she was house-bound, crippled for life, no doctor could cure her. Unfortunately, I think I'd offered too much sympathy on the first occasion she had addressed me (always clad in dressing-gown and slippers). Now she was like a limpet to a rock, telling me in meticulous detail about her lumbago and neuralgia. For over ten years she confided in me about being at death's door (I sometimes wished that electric stair-lift was just an electric chair without the lift). I wanted to get on and tune the piano, of course, but wouldn't be released until her husband called her away on account of her bath being ready. Mr Stagg was the loyal Spaniel in the relationship, giving unconditional love. He did everything, including making me a cup of coffee, which, on the first occasion turned out to be the rarely seen Camp coffee. He'd made this cold, but I managed to drink it. I afterwards explained that I'd meant a drop of cold milk would be sufficient rather than his warming a pan of milk, which he'd offered to do.

His confidential promise given to me on numerous occasions was that if anything should ever happen to him or his wife, the piano would go to me: "You've looked after it for so long, you deserve it… And I know you won't put your fees up." With my car ageing faster and faster, the thought of being able to sell that looming black Bechstein – rather like an enormous coffin – was kept in an envelope in my cerebral file of hopeful memories.

After that first moan about being late, from then on I'd make a point of walking up the garden path just as the clock struck ten o'clock. I knew it was about to strike ten because I'd sat in my car and waited for the Radio 4 pips to sound. The first time of my accurate time-keeping I think Mr Stagg had just presumed that I'd taken heed of his rebuke from the last visit. As the amazingly accurate appointments accumulated, however (and that was an alarming amount of accidental alliteration), there would be an increasing look of admiration-cum-puzzlement on his face. Gleaming comments such as, "Right on time!", "On the dot," "I could set my watch by your visits," would be greeted with a shrug of the shoulders from me and a casual remark about not having my watch on (which I didn't), and then a swift change of conversation. Sometimes I would string it along a bit by looking half-interestedly at the clock on the mantelpiece and remarking, "Oh, so it is dead on ten. That's lucky. I was fortunate in there not being too much traffic on the roads this morning."

In my petty way I'd really left far too early. There was *always* too much traffic on the road as I crawled towards Uxbridge, Ealing, Ealing Common, Ealing Broadway, Ealing Central, West Ealing, Ealing Bored-stiff, etc. I just couldn't be late. I felt like a cop on an early-morning raid, camped outside the target's house, waiting for the signal from ops. Except that if, per chance, the traffic had been light I would drop in at the local cafe and have a tea and read of the paper first. That wasn't often. Usually, with only fifteen minutes to spare I would park a few streets down and urge the car clock to hurry up. 9.45, 9.50, 9.51; the minutes seemed like relentless hours, but eventually the radio would warn that there were six or so minutes to go: 'Coming up to the news', I think the helpful broadcaster Melvyn would remark (Bragg doing his bit for me and Mr Stagg).

It was time to start the car and drive slowly round to the Staggs' place. I knew how many seconds it took to switch the radio off, then the engine, unbelt, lock up and get the case out of the boot. This all had to be done the moment the pips had started. If there were a few extraneous seconds to kill between parking outside his house and walking up the path – probably because I had picked the case up just a fraction too quickly or had got a space immediately outside his house – I could always pretend to be putting the A–Z map away or tidying something in the boot, or (plan C) stop to retie a shoelace. Dangerous things, loose shoelaces.

Even from the place round the corner to his house you had to allow time for such things as learner drivers or the rare chance of there being no parking spaces near his house. No, I couldn't possibly be a minute early or late and destroy the tradition. There would be seven final slabs to cross (only one with a crack) as I strode towards the front door and casually rang the bell. I always arrived to hear the ten o'clock chimes on Mr Stagg's hall clock as he opened the door (lovely things, clocks). It had to be Turner the tuner: on time, every time.

My small pleasure (alright, enormous pleasure) centred around making it look as though I hadn't a care in the world. Any comment about being dead on time was met with a quizzical look and mumbled comment about coincidence or, displaying an air of forgetfulness, "It was about ten you wanted me to come, wasn't it?" Even when making the appointment, without spoiling it by overacting, I would get him to remind me what sort of time he normally liked me to come (feigning ignorance and that, with thousands of other daily appointments, I couldn't possibly remember individual times of certain customers).

Sadly, there came a time when his wife answered the phone and, still quite grief-stricken, told me that Fred had recently died (I don't know how, but she seemed to manage to link his death with my not calling him in the first week of October. It was now the middle of October – he'd always been perfectly happy to have it done 'any time in October' but she felt I was late in ringing). She was at a loss; he'd done everything. But she still thought I should come. It turned out to be the last visit, but Mrs Stagg, although an invalid, was well enough to get dressed and come to the door. She told me Mr Stagg had apparently come in from the garden and collapsed in the kitchen. Fortunately, she'd had her bath and they'd just enjoyed a cup of tea, though the washing-up hadn't been done. Basically, his ticker had unwound for the last time: natural causes, nothing sinister. "Now I don't know what I'll do." It was he, in his faithful Austin Cambridge, kept on after his sales rep days with Sainsbury's, who did the once-a-week trip to the big Sainsbury's (loyal to the end). At seventy-eight, this run was the only journey he dared to make in the busy London traffic.

Mind you, it depends on what you call London; many would say the outskirts of Southall are not in London. Both he and the missus had lived there all their lives. He'd often described the genuine village ambience that had existed there when he was a boy. He could still see in his mind's eye the green fields and streams at the back of his house, now choc-a-bloc with street after street of semi-detached housing. Trying valiantly to avoid regret or bitterness (like so many people nervous of the PC brigade), over time he described the sad though quite fascinating spectacle of fields disappearing, country lanes becoming dangerous roads and rat runs; and of his friends and neighbours, one by one, disappearing to pastures new while Heathrow-bound aeroplanes landed with new inhabitants. The houses with dark-skinned occupants and strange smells had come gradually closer and closer, all-encompassing until, in the last seven years, he and his wife were literally the tiny minority, the only white occupants who lived on that busy road. It sounded like General Custer's Last Stand.

I only visited Mrs Stagg the once after her husband had died, and within a few weeks had a strange phone call. A rather curt man phoning from Dorset explained that he, an accountant and a cousin of Mrs Stagg's, was handling the family's affairs now, and it had been decided to put Aunty into a home. It was very much a one-sided conversation, but he explained that he was doing an audit of all of Aunty's house contents, and asked if I could confirm the commercial value of the piano. I mentioned that I might be interested in it, to which he answered that it wasn't in Southall anymore; he'd had it removed to his house for safe keeping. He said he felt duty bound to look after it and get a good price for it sometime in the future, but that Mrs Stagg was so pleased his daughter was able to make good use of it and had kindly said he could hang on to it for as long as he needed to. He also wondered if I wanted to come down and tune it?

The longer I stayed in piano tuning the more I became acquainted with the inevitable: death. Mr Stagg's death and others of his ilk reminded me of a clock spring slowly unwinding. One that would eventually naturally come to the end of its use and, therefore, life. It could only be used once and that was it; it wasn't supposed to be restarted: lights out, good night and goodbye. Numerous customers described how their partners (often whom I had known) had passed on.

Despite their advanced age and no obvious illness it was still a shock to those left behind. Derek, for example, had been half eating his corn flakes when he let go of the Sunday paper and slowly slumped to the floor. "We'd just shared a joke about something he'd read, and then he was gone." What a nice way to go: little forewarning and no pain. It was really strange developing a relationship with 'Mrs Derek' afterwards. She'd always kept well out of the way when I visited. Music and the piano was his domain. He was a singing teacher. In five years I don't think I had ever even said good morning to her; she always seemed to be hidden away in a backroom or in the kitchen (and it was always Derek who made the tea for me).

Derek's piano was a lovely walnut Bechstein grand, and I had discussed with Derek about having it overhauled. I was surprised, then, that although he had recently departed, Mrs Derek still wanted the piano tuned and also for me to go ahead with the overhauling. I spent a good week in the home restringing it and improving the action. Mrs Derek said she would make a point of playing it from time to time once it was ready so that it wouldn't get ignored or clogged with dust. She also half hoped: "It would be nice for Norman to hear it up there and know it's in tip-top condition."

With those of an older age whom I knew well, I would occasionally sound them out about their thoughts on old age and dying. Did they think they had any regrets, were they ready to go, what did they think happened after death? I was slightly surprised that the men were generally matter-of-fact, some verging on being dismissive. Mr Armada had been typical in this trait (apart from the Christians, though it's surprising just how many of these apparently devout church-going Christians have told me about their wider interests. For example, spiritualism or crossing to another branch of Christianity have featured widely, though they wouldn't like to tell their priest or vicar). Mr Armada was strictly of the opinion that 'when you die you die'; you're put in the ground and that's it. There's no afterlife and no one with a tick sheet of pluses and minuses. There's no second existence of any kind, nothing happens, you won't see your loved ones and you won't come back. If you're in the ground you'll be eaten by worms; if you're cremated, so much the better. You only live life once…

It struck me that perhaps this philosophy was adopted as a useful coping mechanism. It eased the last stages in life. You don't have to worry about meeting your maker. Loved ones are not looking down on you. You may as well get on with life and do what you want to do.

A number of older men who had outlived their spouses (which went against the norm) were quick to find new partners or even get married again at seventy-plus. Once again, the philosophy that there is nothing after this life removes any feelings of guilt, and enables one to move on. Men perhaps more than women found it harder to live without a partner. Someone they've known intimately for decades, each knew what the other was thinking. Now there was an empty space in the bed. The jobs she did so well are now all his. Cooking is for one only, now there is no other. The post still comes for you both, but she or he is now permanently in the past tense. Rosemary used to, Rosemary was. 'Our' ought to be 'My'. Rosemary is now a picture, memory and empty space.

I admired the couples who were devoted to each other. They knew each other's weaknesses but were tolerant and understanding. On the other hand, I grew ever weary of the couples that bickered at each other. I say couples, though it was usually one half of the couple who did all the snapping and sarcasm. They too were probably devoted to each other but I dislike people who put their partners down in front of visitors. "He's got better things to do than stand talking to you, dear." "I'm sorry, she's a right bore, isn't she?" "He can't do anything in the house, absolutely useless." Even worse is when parents shut their children up, not allowing them to speak or utter an opinion. I'm not talking about noisy children who pester you and won't let you get on with your work; I'm thinking of the adult who thinks he or she is the only expert (or person) worth talking to. I should point out here that, where children are concerned, there is a trait for middle-class parents to draw their off-spring's attention to you. Leoni is called into the room and encouraged (on the first visit) to watch the craftsman, learn how a piano actually functions. Working-class children will either come in of their own volition (with parents warning them not to be a nuisance) or they will ignore you completely. Where the death had been due to a lingering illness, I found myself on numerous occasions in a difficult situation. You're never sure whether to mention the partner or how much should be said. I've been told that most relatives of recently deceased loved ones do actually want visitors and friends to talk about them; they want their loved ones to be remembered. I play it by ear and wait for the right cues. In my situation I have found myself in the blurred position of visitor, family friend and service provider.

On numerous occasions I have witnessed the embarrassing though understandable position of the partner breaking down in front of me. The man who has lost his wife to cancer calls me after a respectful period of time (though I find it really difficult if they are telling you the news for the first time over the phone. 'Sorry' or 'My condolences' seem so meaningless, no matter how genuinely you might mean it). Upon meeting the partner, all seems to be going well; he shakes your hand and smiles at the door. He potters around, makes you a cup of tea. All goes well until a flash of memory or fleeting reference to her stabs away with overpowering grief. Uncontrollable tears start to roll down his cheeks. You've never seen this grown man as you see him now. The retired pilot or policeman apologises, though you don't want him to. He has to leave the room. Is it crass to carry on tuning? Do you go after him, embrace him, or will that make him and you more embarrassed? Being men, you tend to give each other space, carry on, and you both later act as though nothing has happened. Trouble is, I can always see it when someone has lost a loved one. Their eyes are haunted; they are in shock even six months after. They can never be the same again.

Dr Naylor described to me how his wife had been taken with breast cancer. I'd known her well, hadn't even met Dr Naylor as he was always at work. It was quite a shock when he answered the phone and, sounding reasonably composed, explained that Mrs Naylor, despite the best treatment, had been taken within a few months (I hadn't even known that she was ill).

It was rather strange the first time we met. I'd heard all about him and he knew of 'Mr Turner, the piano tuner'. On the first meeting we inevitably started talking about Mrs Naylor: Dr Naylor's partner, no longer here but someone known well to both of us. He didn't break down; he spoke of carrying on, keeping most things normal for the sake of his youngest boy, who was still at school. I imagined it must have been particularly hard for him, a doctor, not able to save his own wife. I know his son was in awe of him; he spoke often of his dad and how his dad knew just about everything there was to know about the world. I could imagine Dr Naylor going to the ends of the earth to get the right treatment for his wife. Sadly, it had happened ten years too early, before much-improved early detection and treatment plans were the norm.

We didn't dwell on Mrs Naylor for long, though he did confide in me some of his thoughts on death. Being a doctor, he'd seen death often, wasn't afraid of it. Yes it could be hair-raising when, as a police doctor, he thought he couldn't stop the bleeding of a major artery. Blood pouring everywhere and him panicking inside. Later in his work, he said he had often had to counsel grieving patients whose partners had died, and help them get on with life. Only now, he admitted, did he really know and understand what grief was. He confided that he'd truly no idea of the unbearable pain and sense of loss his patients must have been going through.

On later visits Dr Naylor was practical in his approach to his wife's death. Initially, Dr Naylor's attitude to his wife's death was that she was gone, here no more. Yes he missed her and thought about her from time to time, but there was no afterlife; she was not waiting for him. That was the end, he will find new things to do, life must go on. He would take up the violin again, and get out socially. True to his word, after a year he was going steady with a former patient, a nice Italian lady (though it didn't lead anywhere special).

He always insisted on making me a cup of tea (strangely something his wife had never done. Although I come across men at home less frequently than women, men always seem to play the role of host more reliably. If people like Mrs Naylor didn't make you a cup of tea, at least you knew where you stood, and I certainly wouldn't want to be swimming in tea every day. On the other hand, if everyone was from the same school of thought as Mrs Naylor, I'd live a very parched life).

As the years passed, Dr Naylor had almost completely retired. He still kept himself busy but had given up driving. Thus, even going to the local shops – which weren't very local – entailed getting used to buses. I don't know how it came about but, when talking about buses and shops, I inadvertently learnt that his new freedom was somewhat curtailed. Not so much by money but by local circumstances. He'd been a keen concert-goer but had chosen to give up travelling to London for evening concerts after having an unpleasant experience with a drunk at the station. Worse still, for him and many other people of his generation, he explained that the buses are out of bounds after 3.30pm. "Travel at your peril," he shuddered, and went on to explain that the offensive language and aggressive barging and pushing of the school children travelling home made bus stops and the local shops 'no-go' areas (and he didn't even live in what people tend to categorise as a 'rough area'). He wasn't complaining to me; he said it almost in passing, as though everybody knew. I felt so sad that someone who has worked all their life (actually his father had been a train driver, so Dr Naylor had struggled to get himself into and through medical school), served in the war, and brought up a son and daughter after his partner had died, should have their choices and freedom taken away.

I hadn't minded Dr Naylor's wife not making tea: it was much better than the mental cruelty of being offered a cup and it never appearing. I once had a female customer who, in her distant childhood, had been given too much of the wrong sort of anaesthetic gas at the dentist, leaving her, she explained, with permanent loss of short-term memory. She never went far without her notepad and pencil. Three times she came in and asked if she'd offered me a cup of tea. Three times I'd given the answer, "Yes," and that it was milk no sugar, thank you. It never appeared. After the end of an hour and a half's long slog on her recalcitrant piano, I popped my head round the door and gave her my bill. "I *did* give you your cup of tea, didn't I?" I couldn't bring myself to say no. "Yes. And very lovely it was too." Her faced beamed. "Marvellous. Only did I tell you that I was once given too much anaesthetic at the dentist and that…"

Miss Ogden-Price was much older than Dr Naylor when I first knew her. She had turned ninety but was far from lonely. She seemed to be permanently bent double; without wishing to be uncharitable, it looked as though she was one of those figures with leathery skin and a sagging chest that had been dug out of an ancient peat bog. You could nearly see right through her coat-hanger frame but she was a very good egg. Had all her own faculties.

Miss Ogden-Price is perhaps the only customer with a double-barrelled name with whom I didn't play my petty game. If someone was known as (for example) Mr Hickory-Smith, I don't know why but I could seldom resist feigning ignorance and asking over the telephone, "May I speak to Mr Smith, please?" A curt, "It's Hickory-Smith, actually" (or even Lord Hickory-Smith) would be volleyed back to me, where I, in turn, with a mystified apology, as though putting my specs on, would answer, "Oh… I thought it said Hilary Smith. So sorry." People with such names as Lewington-Jones are either Lewington or Jones, in my book; they can't be both (or not at the same time). I'm just waiting for the scales to be tipped to the point when just about everyone in society has adopted a double-barrelled name and we will see the even more tedious spread of triple-barrelled surnames. I've got mine lined up as Mr Jonathan Constable-Turner-Smythe. (Present company – those possessing double-barrelled names – naturally, may be excused… Or better still, sort yourself out and decide which *one* name you will use for a proper, non-greedy, unpretentious, unostentatious surname.)

The nice Miss Ogden-Price, witness of two world wars and the rise and fall of the M25, had not lead a sheltered life. Not a great pianist, she'd literally only gone into Harrods to buy some tomatoes from the food hall but landed up ordering a small upright. The famous Harrods sale was on and certain pianos were apparently ridiculously cheap. With few family ties she had done more than her fair share of charity work over the years (had also driven ambulances during the last war). She wanted a piano more for when her nephew and niece visited.

She was a modest old lady who still helped 'the elderly' and local friends when she could. On first appearances, helping an African student fulfil his dream may seem like a tall story, but I took her at her word and it only cropped up in conversation because she was reminded of it when looking in her diary and fixing our next appointment.

Miss O-P was written to out of the blue from a young man in Africa. The story, as she told it to me, was that this young man was desperate to better himself. He wanted to learn accountancy but had not the means to pay for his education, nor knew of a suitable place in which to study. He'd been told by an elder chief that England was the place to go for such things. The wise heads among his people had thought that, though a slim chance, someone in England might be prepared to sponsor him. Somehow they'd got hold of a special book given to people in London – this large book contained all their telephone numbers – so these people were undoubtedly rich. Importantly, many of the people in this impressive (and rather thick) book lived near the Queen. He chose at random a name from the book and composed the best letter he could. Fortuitously, it was addressed to an important lady called Ogden, who, after many weeks sent a reply asking for more information.

By the time I'd met Miss O-P, the student was staying in digs in London and was half-way through his accountancy training. Although he had a grant of sorts, the admirable Miss O-P had met him and was still making regular payments to finance his board and lodgings, and acting as a sort of mentor in a variety of ways.

By the time Miss O-P was on my books I was heading towards becoming a veteran piano tuner. The beard had gone down the sink long ago. Pushing forty, I was 'old' and wanted to look younger. Irritatingly, the so-called teenage acne hadn't vanished altogether. An excruciatingly embarrassing spot would erupt from time to time, encouraging the hobbyist dermatologists to regale me with 'correct' advice: wash more frequently; don't wash, it aggravates the skin; stop eating chocolate; squirt lemon juice on it; you must drink at least twenty litres of carrot juice every two hours.

Oxyten, I think it was called, the saviour of many a teenager, was a powerful blitzer of spots. The way I used it, it rapidly destroyed the glaring red or green-pussed spot, but seemed to sand-blast away many layers of fragile skin too. I remember waking up one morning to find, after a glorious few months of spot-free skin, the beginnings of yet another eruption right on my forehead. I couldn't possibly call on Mrs Ashley with that on my face. She lived in a plush apartment close to where the ex-Prime Minister Harold Wilson had his London residence. (I once saw him shambling along Victoria Street. He'd long since been out of the limelight. It needed a second look. He was a tiny, solitary figure walking about almost aimlessly. No one gave him a second look. I believe he later had dementia.)

My only hope for Mrs Ashley was to have a good wash and then leave a generous dab of Oxyten to do its work. It was a pure white concoction (rather like putting Tippex on your face), but it was worth leaving on my face while I drove up to Victoria. I would find a parking meter and then wipe it off at the last moment. With God on my side it might have started to eat into the offending eruption and reduced the volcano to a dry, insignificant bump. Perhaps I'd say, if asked, I got the bump in a rugby scrum; that would sound honourable.

The journey, for morning rush hour, wasn't too bad and I'd become quite an expert at finding lesser-known parking meters. Mrs Ashley proved to be her chirpy self. I'd also survived the lift again. For such a high-class block it had an ancient lift, the type with the folding zig-zag doors inviting children to poke their hands through (just the once!). It had broken down once, on a previous visit, whilst I was its solitary passenger, just as it was nearing the ground floor. The caretaker, a huge man, seemed to be quite used to this and heard the faint calls of a lost lamb. He shouted something about helping me rather than waiting a couple of hours for an engineer to come out. As he came over

I could see most of his top half through the doors, the floor of the lift being about level with his shoulders. He forced the doors open and asked me to pass my case down. I then had the ignominious experience of being manhandled (rugby after all!) around the upper legs and half dragged and half lifted down on to the floor of the lobby. Fortunately he was swift, but I couldn't help wondering what would happen if the lift suddenly came into action and moved upwards with me half in and half out.

With Mrs Ashley, in no time at all I was half-way through the piano and she came in and left a welcome cup of tea and biscuits. Stretching my legs, I sipped the tea as I was sauntering around the room. Nice photo here, interesting book there… the ornament in front of the large mirror caught my eye until, horror! the white blob also caught my eye in the mirror. Good old Mrs Ashley hadn't said a word, hadn't batted an eyelid. Far too polite. Even after I had removed it, when she came back into the room a short while later, I couldn't detect anything other than her usual homely expression. Did she wonder if it was toothpaste? Maybe I'd been greedily tucking into a fresh cream cake before her visit. What was I doing with that ping pong ball on my forehead? Maybe I was making a mountain out of a mole hill (well, the spot was related to moles, sort of)?

I'd been lucky in having a busy round, built up over many years. Even managed to have five people in the same road once, and some weren't aware that 'our piano tuner' was also 'theirs'. In one instance I had to be careful not to take sides. In a long road that backed on to the Thames over Hampton Court way, I'd tuned the piano at number 82 for quite a few years, then, through an obscure contact, began tuning for the people next door at number 84. They'd been searching for a tuner for ages without success. With them both becoming part of my client list, neither of these two neighbours would ever say much about each other, just a polite smile and forced, "Oh, yes?" could be elicited if I ever mentioned that I had been tuning (or was going to tune) next door's. The young girl of the parents at number 84 once let the cat partly out the bag when her parents were out of earshot. Raising her eyebrows in an almost identical way to her mother, she began to tell me about 'the boring fuddy duddies' next door. "All he ever does is go up and down the river in his silly little boat. Yet just because once Daddy parked…" I don't think it was coincidental, but the conversation was cut short by her mum sweeping in and announcing with unusually heightened excitement that there was a sparrow in the garden. Still, it meant that I was always well looked after, both neighbours wanting to create a good impression and not wanting to give the other something to talk about. Prompt payment along with tea and cakes were always guaranteed at numbers 82 and 84.

The little girl at number 84 was like many of her age, full of questions: what are you doing? Why does it need tuning? How do you tune a piano? What's that thing in your mouth? It must have looked a bit strange, for although not every piano tuner did it that way, after striking the prongs of the tuning fork I would quickly place the non-vibrating part of the fork between my teeth. This way it sounded crystal clear and my hands were free to strike the key and turn the tuning lever. It was important to get that first pitch right as all the other notes would be tuned in correct relation to it. I often had to think of simple answers that would satisfy these inquisitive youngsters; I normally needed them to go away after a bit otherwise I'd never get the job done. On the other hand, if I was in no rush, I would indulge them a little. For example, to get at the years of accumulated dust (which was particles and fibres of piano felt as well as dust) under the keyboard, I would pull the black and white keys right out. They would sit on the piano's lid like a set of grinning teeth. In the shallow chasm left in the key-bed, hoovering was always done carefully, as one occasionally came across farthings or jewellery that, over the years, had slipped between the keys. Handing children assortments of ancient negatives, old hair grips and occasional coins made me into a temporary magician. The height of fascination for one curious boy was my retrieving a skeleton of a long-deceased mouse. Slightly crushed, it was straightened out and royally displayed in his bedroom in minutes. (Had it been listening to 'Marche funèbre'?)

I was always careful, of course, to answer questions posed by children cautiously. I'd only once made the mistake of telling a little girl that the grand piano's peculiar kidney shape was specially designed that way to accommodate fat solo soprano opera singers. The maid had let me in that day; I wasn't to know that mummy was an extra-large opera singer. Fortunately, I don't think the little girl had understood 'soprano', the joke had gone over her head and she was too interested in what Mummy had bought from Selfridges, but I considered it something of a close shave.

I later learnt that piano tuning wasn't as lucrative as it had been once, or so the old boys in the trade told me. Pass any home in the late 1940s, chances are that most had a piano but very few a television. For many owners, the convention was to have it tuned three, if not four, times a year (each change of season), whereas now it is more likely to be once or twice. Christmas time, they said, was always a frantic time: schools and churches wanted it done for the annual carol service or concert, and most other house owners (and pubs) 'must' have the piano tuned for their own singsongs and New Year celebrations. Much quieter now, with electric keyboards, karaoke machines and CDs. A piano is a rather more rare birthday or Christmas gift nowadays, though I once had to tune a new upright which had been hidden in what was not much more than a broom cupboard.

I was invited in rather secretively by the parents on 24th December, who then asked the son to take the dog for a long walk in a frosty park, which he was rather annoyed about (I think he thought I was the meter reader). "Take your time!" they called out to him, whilst imploring me in whispered tones: "Be as quick as you can."

Evidently not as financially rewarding as the 1940s, I still found the run-up to Christmas could get hectic, though I needed it to be lucrative as work after Christmas was inevitably – like much of the festive wine and pop – either stale or flat. It always seemed to be my luck that whatever car I happened to be running at the time would decide to let me down in mid-December. Just when I needed to get around quickly, and there were last-minute appointments, the car would develop a fault. And there was nothing worse than having said a polite goodbye to a well-off customer, only for them pretending not to notice me through the window trying to get a stubborn car to start.

Looking as cool as a cucumber – my body language suggesting that the car always took a little while to start on frosty mornings, didn't it? – but inwardly shouting expletives, I just couldn't bear Mr Reeves-Draper to come scrunching down the drive with Gold and Sovereign, his two 'harmless' Alsatians. He'd see the mess in the car but pretend not to notice it: "The old girl playing you up? …You *are* a member of the AA, aren't you? I've been a member for forty years." Other younger clientele would mutter something about flooded carburetors, or ask if I was in the RAC. One or two dry, 'funny' comments were harder to take: "Needs a bit of tuning, hey?" All I wanted was for the wretched car to start so that I would not be left stranded.

Garages, alas, if not closing early for Christmas, were inundated with last-minute urgent requests. My Christmas bonus, as it were, was frequently swallowed up by a heavy bill to fix the car. Still, mince pies and seasonal good cheer, along with occasional extra tips, compensated to a degree (apart from the few of my customers who were Jehovah's Witnesses – very nice people, but not a Christmas card or mince pie in sight, or at least not until Jesus himself decides to return).

No, it seems that I'd generally missed the piano's peak of popularity, when it would be pushed out into the street for a singsong at the drop of a hat. But I'd also missed its brief big fall from favour. About the 1960s and early 1970s, many pianos, it seemed, couldn't be given away. It was cheaper to run ageing cruise ship pianos over the side (burial at sea) rather than trade them in. Village fetes saw the spectacle of handcrafted instruments being wheeled unceremoniously onto the green for the next piano-smashing contest. Others were viciously assaulted and made into such things as drinks cabinets or writing bureaus. A far cry from the earliest days when pianos were a status symbol and had been one of the first things – if not the first – to become available on HP. Grands were a trifle too sexy for Victorians, of course, who thought it only right and proper to keep the three legs modestly covered with appropriate material.

For most of my career pianos have been in fashion again. Be it the television studio who are always panicking and wanting it done urgently between recordings, or a mansion or bedsit, or even just a Barnes piano for Mr Barnes, I've enjoyed getting out and about rather than travelling to the office five days a week. The said Mr Barnes wasn't joking when he said he had a Barnes upright, and, yes, he really did live in Barnes.

There was also the chance to earn a bit extra occasionally. Putting right the piano that the mad Professor Rose had ruined, for example. I don't know what he was a professor of exactly, possibly he wasn't an actual professor at all, but that is how he styled himself; he was known to be able to talk the hind legs off a piano owner if not a donkey. Didn't have a clue how to tune or repair a piano, though apparently impressed customers with his playing. Sadly, he ruined many a piano by giving the action copious squirts with his oil can. His one and only answer to any mechanical problem in the piano was to oil everything, regardless of whether it was made of metal, plastic or wood. A mention on Ester Rantzen's watchdog style programme, *That's Life*, had, if anything, the wrong effect, only serving to bolster his ego.

Amazingly, Professor Rose would often walk the streets of south London and surrounding counties of Kent and Surrey, and peer into homeowners' front windows. If he spotted a piano he would be at the door with his well-rehearsed spiel: "I just happened to be passing and I couldn't help noticing the lovely piano in the window… Have you had it tuned recently? …Not an ideal place to keep it, near the window, goes out of tune very quickly, you know…" Professor Rose also had the cunning idea of, having 'tuned' the piano, suggesting the customer did not try it straight away: "Don't touch it yet! Must give it a chance to settle for a day or two." A chance for him to get away, more likely.

He was not the only tuner peddling such housewives' tips (or housewives' myths?). Other tips included cleaning the ivories with milk, which sounds plausible but was neither hygienic nor effective. A touch of methylated spirits, on the other hand, can be more effective, and also for reviving polished piano cases (or some French polishers often used to recommend giving it a rub over with a solution of vinegar and water). One or two elderly customers, who had spent childhoods in distant countries, told me of piano owners who stood their grand pianos in bowls of salt, to stop the ants or other insects crawling up the piano legs and into the piano. Or in the monsoon season, apparently, one owner kept a tray of burning charcoal under her piano to stop the damp getting in.

Incidentally, after a random perusal of county newspapers which were available at my local library (they had a selection going back a hundred years or more), I discovered that stories of 'imposter piano tuners' was a fairly frequent occurrence, be it 1880 or 1980. Men would go around claiming to be a piano tuner when they weren't. Some would take extra money from customers after claiming more repairs were needed, but despite promising to return to complete the work the next day would then disappear. Times of hardship – after a period of war or during the depression and high unemployment – tended to see an increase in the prevalence of these bogus piano tuners.

I managed to rescue one customer's stash of 'readies' once after discovering the hidden money in the bottom part of his upright piano. It transpired that Professor Rose had visited. The customer thought he ought to be good if he was a professor. The 'Professor tuner' could certainly play well but the piano hadn't worked or sounded quite right after he'd gone. He left me to get on with it, hoping I could get it back to normal again. I saw the tell-tale signs in the action, which was very sluggish, and pulled out the bottom panel to do a thorough investigation of the whole piano. There, in a dark corner of the piano was a parcel of grimy newspaper dripping in oil. I removed the string and layers of oily paper until I reached the final layer, which was fortunately just about dry. Untouched, was a large wad of notes which must have amounted to several thousand pounds. What it was doing there I don't know. When the owner came into the room, I suggested he change the hiding place. Somewhat embarrassed though relieved, he searched for a biscuit tin. I had a harder time explaining that a lot of those readies would be needed to undo the work from the professor's recent visit.

I did contact my local newspaper suggesting they should warn piano owners about people (or 'tuners') making impromptu visits or the damage oiling piano action parts can do. It proved to be a rather fruitless exercise as the reporter was more concerned about the newspaper getting embroiled in legal action if they somehow identified a certain person (not that they had to actually name names); it seemed that if they couldn't make a 'story' out of it, they weren't prepared to do a public service kind of report and so nothing came of my tip-off (Professor Rose, oil can in hand, happily went about his business for a number of more years after this).

What with people still sleeping in their beds, other customers asking me to tune pianos squeezed into trailers or sheds at the bottom of gardens, or a few customers who thought it quite alright to have a blazing row with their partners whilst the tuner tuned (or attempted to tune) the piano, it was all par for the course as far as I was concerned. I could handle most of them now, even those who insisted the very bottom bass notes weren't tuned properly (they were, but on cheap and nasty pianos the extreme bass notes sound rather grotty even when they are in tune). A colleague of mine told me how he often indulged the customer in these situations by playing the note and asking the querying customer if the note should be taken up a bit (made sharp) or taken down. He would move the tuning lever and adjust the string according to the customer's directions. With the customer happy, the tuner was happy and got his money. In reality he hadn't altered the tuning at all: just moved (or wobbled) the lever a little while striking the key, and as there was a bit of play in the lever, it looked as though he was resetting/turning the tuning pin. He'd put on a bit of a show and the customer was convinced that the string was now in tune. In most cases you tune the customer and not the piano!

Take your money and run, sadly, became one of my mottos, as some customers would not listen to advice. Even though they were told it wasn't worth tuning, or they shouldn't pay what was being asked for a certain piano, they knew better: they liked the colour, or, presumably, they thought I had magical powers and would be able to make everything alright. The biggest risk some customers take is buying pianos at an auction: at least get it checked over by someone as it may be in the auction because it has a fault and is almost unsellable in the trade. (I once came across an unsellable Steinway upright that someone had recently acquired but wanted to sell because it didn't sound 'that great'. The fall – lid over the keyboard – had the genuine inlaid Steinway name, but a quick look inside showed it wasn't a Steinway at all, just a mediocre mass-produced upright, so insignificant there wasn't even a name on the iron frame. Steinfake would have been more appropriate.)

Fortunately, Mr Warner (we'll call him) had no problems with his lovely mahogany Steinway grand. I soon learnt that he'd been a famous conductor, a fact made obvious by the numerous photographs that depicted him in stylish tuxedo and bow tie conducting huge orchestras at the Albert Hall and elsewhere. This was a Harrods client, and when I'd knocked on the door, the distinguished gentleman, in his sixties, answered the door. I can't recall exactly how the welcome and introduction went, but he just seemed very vague. He seemed to understand but didn't say much that made any sense. He obviously had other things on his mind. I felt I could have said I was the bank manager or milkman, and he still would have let me in. He shuffled off and disappeared into the back of the apartment somewhere; I found his piano in one of the rooms so commenced tuning it. Halfway during the tuning, Mrs Warner appeared from nowhere and offered me a cup of coffee. She was quite used to explaining about her husband. Matter-of-factly, she told me that Gus had received a bump on his head and had never been right since, having to retire rather abruptly.

He came in occasionally whilst I was tuning, always smiling and affable, but any attempts by me at conversation were futile. He could talk in sentences, but not one word uttered made the slightest sense. I'm not sure he even knew his way around the apartment. Nor, possibly, what time it was, as I hadn't noticed when he first let me in that he was still in his pyjamas and dressing gown at midday. I've no doubt the Steinway had once been used a good deal (in fact Mrs Warner later told me that many famous singers and performers used to rehearse on it with Gus before big concerts), but it was clear that it had been surplus to requirements for a long while now. What I did notice, strangely, was that when I played part of the *Pathetique* sonata at the end, to test the tuning – but also because quality pianos inspire me to play – Mr Warner appeared like magic and gave me a broad smile and reassuring pat on the shoulder. A wave of recognition had spread across his face, he didn't need to tell me, he was humming along nicely in tune and conducting – in perfect time – while I played. I could understand now why Mrs Warner wasn't as upset as I'd expected her to be. She and he hadn't lost everything (in hindsight, I suspect he had dementia).

My brief spell with the ambulance and buying and selling pianos had told me early on that piano dealing, as such, was not for me. On the other hand, I would inspect pianos for prospective buyers, and earned a small commission when putting the right people in contact with each other. It's always better to get a qualified person to look at a piano rather than leave it to chance. Many is the time I've seen 'bargains' bought privately or in auction that turn out to have cracked frames or bogus heritage. If it's really cheap, ask why; and if it's really expensive, ask why. Perhaps like no other trade, pianos can fetch amazing prices depending on: the make/model, finish of the casework, age, the time of year, the seller's or buyer's status, the urgency (or lack of it) to sell/buy the said piano, the geographical location of it, and knowledge or ignorance of one or both parties. Occasionally, the emotional appeal can also win favour: a good home is desired for the piano rather than simply the highest price; or the crippled, divorced lady's sweet child (only child) with enormous talent has been offered free lessons, on condition that she has a good piano to practise on. She has very little money, of course, but there is always hope…

One customer described to me how he once got a morsel of satisfaction back after buying a piano that really wasn't any good, from a high-street music shop. The salesman, unbeknown to the customer at the time, wanted to get rid of a new though unusual Irish piano he had in stock. The manufacturers claimed it would last for years. All the parts were made from plastic, so you could even play it under water, apparently. Most people in the trade know this particular piano is not very good. In a short period of time the plastic bits get brittle and start to break. They are not easy pianos to fix, especially as the parts are unique and spares very difficult to find. (These pianos don't even sound particularly nice when they are working.)

The customer, seeing the shiny upright piano in the window, was pleased that it was greatly reduced in price and, after listening to the salesman's eager promotion of the said piano, bought it there and then for his daughter. In only a few years his daughter had progressed very well and really outgrown the piano. Actually, they wished they'd never bought it, as it had had niggling faults and proved to be very unreliable. On the advice of his daughter's piano teacher, he phoned the showroom and said he had a second-hand piano for sale and was thinking about trading it in for a new one. The salesman had not remembered the customer (though the customer recognised the salesman's voice all too well) and asked for the particulars of the piano. Upon hearing it was one of those Irish pianos he replied, "No, sir, we couldn't give you anything for that, I'm afraid," to which the customer enquired why not. He received the answer, "We don't touch them with a barge pole… Nothing but trouble." The customer bellowed down the phone, "Well, why did you sell it to me then, Mr Jones!"

A colleague had opened a new branch of his piano showrooms in north London. Although out of my way, he was able to line up a day's worth of customers every couple of months or so to make it worth my while coming over. It was still a bit of a drudge, though: sitting on the A406 North Circular on a boiling hot day, smog everywhere, my knee creaking and clicking with the constant clutch in, first gear, clutch out, creep a metre, wait for another few minutes... Although a very long day, it was better once I got used to leaving really early to avoid the rush hour, then leaving quite late at the end of the day for the same reason.

On one of these occasional trips, having managed to get over the equator quite well (the river that separates the south Londoners from an entirely different tribe north of the Thames), I was three quarters the way towards my first customer, the first of many crammed in that day (tiring but financially rewarding), when a horrible feeling hit me. Whilst nearing 'Billionaires' Row' (a remarkable avenue of sixty-six mansions over Hampstead and East Finchley way owned by the rich and famous – including the actor Gordon Jackson. It was strange him letting me in once to tune his piano, and he wasn't even in his butler of *Upstairs, Downstairs* garb), I was still crawling along at a steady ten miles per hour, when I groped behind my seat for my trusty attaché case which contained all my tools. Of course it wasn't there; every night I always locked it in the boot so that it would be safe and ready for the next day – it would be in the boot, wouldn't it? (I'd only needed the harsh lesson once of having it stolen from the backseat – I've always wondered what the thief expected to find after he'd taken it round the corner somewhere: a doctor's array of drugs, a wad of notes and business contacts? What would the thief make of a strange rubber wedge or two, some yellowed ivory tops, a small pot of vaseline and a middle C tuning fork – a sorry tune indeed for him?)

I parked the car and, trying to ignore the nagging doubt, checked the boot for my case. It wasn't there. I knew it wasn't there because, as a one-off, I'd taken it indoors the previous night when I'd needed a screwdriver to do a domestic job in the house. That morning, not having the daily habit of carrying it down to the car, I'd unintentionally left the case in the hallway.

Travelling to a day's worth of customers without tools was no good. I couldn't really turn round and go back; the morning rush hour operated both ways and would be even worse now the first school runs were beginning to prowl. I'd be so late that I'd have to cancel the morning ones and make a start on the afternoon ones – making it hardly worth travelling over for. Ringing them and making new appointments would be a pain as well (there were no mobile phones then, only public call boxes where, on the law of averages, the first one would be vandalised; the second occupied with a customer with a bag full of coins ready for a morning's calls from his 'office'; and the third, if it was working and unoccupied, would be decorated with call cards, cigarettes butts, bags of cold chips and have a fragrance of alcoholic urine). Lastly, I couldn't bring myself to call the expectant customers and say I couldn't come because I'd forgotten my tools. I couldn't do that! Does an electrician ever turn up and say he's forgotten his tools?

No, this was a major dilemma until I had one final thought. I could nip in to see my colleague, the piano showroom owner, whose customers I was supposed to be visiting. He did occasional repair work to his pianos himself – I would make a minor detour and cadge a few basic tools off him. Fortunately I was in luck that day; he was in early and I was able to relieve him of a few basic tools. I managed to get through the customers without any hiccups, though I doubt the new customers were that impressed with me turning up with a plastic Waitrose bag full of tools (well, I was a quality tuner at least; it wasn't a Co-op bag).

And so it was that I discovered the Jewish lady who lived in a nearby north London suburb of that great golden, Volvo city, known as Golders Green (or was it Goldstein Green?). She seemed to be the spitting image of the Doreen character in the rather excruciating television sitcom *Birds of a Feather*. She was nice enough if a little too strident in looks and voice (tended to shout down the telephone). Keeping an impeccable home, it was mandatory to adopt the Japanese habit of leaving your shoes in the porch. Mrs Steinberger obviously idolised her family; silver framed photos of 'the boys' were everywhere. Husband apparently worked all hours as an automobile executive (he sold cheap Japanese cars at the local garage) and Mrs Steinberger did her duty at home: keeping herself and the house beautiful for her husband and boys.

Killing two birds with one stone, she would always have the beautician round at the same time as I was tuning the glossy upright piano – Wednesdays were Mrs Steinberger's trades and services day. She was reliable in offering a cup of tea half-way through. We'd sit in the kitchen (no food allowed in the living room) while the lady finished her nails. A biscuit with a, "Leave it if you don't want it," comment would be secreted on the saucer (different to housewives from Beckenham and elsewhere, who tended to leave a plate full of biscuits on the tray). I would find it slightly unnerving sitting there with all the beautician's manicure items, towels and paraphernalia scattered on the table. After a polite good morning they would ignore me and continue with their important though secretive conversation. I didn't particularly want to listen but heard the occasional snippet that didn't really seem to be of worldly importance to me: "…Should have seen what she had in her basket… Daniel's only interested in the bar mitzvah because of the presents… Are yours heavy? Mine used to be dreadful… Oh, the pain… Have you tried…"

After quite a few years' service, when it was eventually time to ask for my (very slightly raised) fee I had grown used to her always querying the amount: "It wasn't that much last time was it? What about customer loyalty, doesn't that stand for anything these days? How long have you been coming here? It's a good piano, you said so yourself!" Sadly, it had never gone up when it should have done. Being a coward and knowing she would argue over the price, it never went up, so when I did finally want to put it up, I suppose she'd become set in her ways. The manicurist, who was there for no more than half an hour each time, was very good at nodding her head and agreeing with everything Mrs Steinberger said (yet she was always there for a shorter time than me but charged a higher fee!).

When her youngest son had reached sixteen and it was obvious he was not going to continue lessons now that he'd more or less got everything he wanted after being bribed to take over the pianist mantle from his brother, Mrs S chatted me up over finding a customer before it depreciated in value any more. She remembered exactly how much this model was worth when new – though she didn't know that I knew she had knocked my colleague right down in price. To get her off the phone, my colleague had reluctantly slashed the price of a brand-new piano and thrown in free delivery. That, apparently, wasn't much of a deal, so an expensive new matching stool had been added to make her happy. Well, she would be happy and not have the distress of going begging to her husband if the first tuning was included in the price too. It wasn't for her, after all; it was for David, who was very talented and had just got into his new school where the fees were exorbitant. (And how were we – the adults – ever going to encourage the next generation of musicians if we didn't provide cheap enough pianos?)

I was circumspect about its value and what she had really paid for it. Although not a normal part of the tuning service, I inspected the piano thoroughly and signed her piece of paper to say I could vouch for the instrument. I left with her reminding me that I would get commission if I could help her find a buyer. Later in the week, I sent her two typed examples of how an advertisement for the piano could be written (providing the necessary technical information serious buyers would ask for).

Two months passed and she hadn't sold it. Fortunately, I remembered a customer who wanted to upgrade their instrument, so I recommended it to them. They were nice people. He was a Sir (knighted for something or other), though they were both very down-to-earth types, speaking in a refined way without sounding overly posh. 'Come back' sounded as it should – 'come back' and not 'come beck'. 'Off' was not 'orf' and 'town' was not 'tyne', which is how older clients living closer to Harrods often enunciated their words.

It turned out they were very pleased with the piano and hadn't haggled over the price. I said nothing about the true price Mrs S had actually paid for it (much below the RRP). They were happy so I looked forward to a little commission from its original owner in due course.

After a month, it occurred to me that Mrs S might have mislaid my address so I decided to give her a ring. I'd got it all wrong, apparently; the onus was on the buyer to pay the commission, as I'd got them a real bargain. She kept going on about the couple who had come to look at it (and eventually bought it), saying they were the 'right people': "They were class. As soon as they walked in I could tell they were class… No, honey, you'll have to chase them up for your commission. You won't have a problem, lovely people."

I later met a Jew who seemed to be right at the bottom of the social scale. He lived by himself in a tiny and rather dilapidated council flat in a poorer quarter of north London. I wouldn't have taken him for a Jew (there was not the usual clue seen over the doorway or symbols in the window), but he seemed to take me for one, asking keenly, "Are you a yid too?"

This likeable old boy had fallen on hard times. He'd apparently trod the boards in his younger days. I wasn't sure what as, but with his bald head, braces and large feet he seemed to have the makings of a good clown. His First World War piano was what I'd heard others in the trade describe as an old fart-box when out of customer earshot. He had no tea or coffee in the house, so looked deep into a barren-looking cupboard and offered me a tomato cup-a-soup instead. I declined this, though appreciated being offered something.

With these old types of piano, invariably belonging to impecunious owners, a vicious cycle exists. They were made before the advent of central heating, which makes them suffer badly in modern times. They were from the bottom end of the market when new, so are not of a quality designed to be hardy and long-lasting. Now aged, such pianos go out of tune more quickly than others and tend to fall apart at the drop of a hat. Although they need more tuning and TLC than other pianos, their customers rarely have the means to tune and service them regularly. Consequently, this one, like many others, was on its last legs. Nonetheless, I tuned it as best I could and, seeing he was an OAP, didn't charge for doing two urgent repairs.

He seemed pleased with it as he tried over some music hall numbers. As a closing party piece he broke into song whilst accompanying himself, which seemed to be reaching some sort of climax. On the closing word of the song he escalated up to a terrible caterwauling pitch. I thought it was part of his comedy act, but he looked at me proudly and exclaimed, "There!" Puzzlement must have crossed my face, as he hit the same high note on the piano and shrieked the same noise again. Triumphantly, he called out, "Top C! I can still hit a top C after all these years – what do you think of that then!" It hadn't been singing as defined by most people, nor was it really a top C, as the piano was a long way down from concert pitch, but he looked so satisfied that I could only look impressed and encouraging. It was nice to see his face still beaming as he led me to the door, asking one more time, "Are you sure you're not a yid? …What's your mother's name?"

TUESDAY 28TH JANUARY

10.00am, Mrs Lewis

I know I can't do Mrs Lewis before 10.00am. She doesn't want to risk the window cleaner being there as, on one occasion, she explained quietly that the reason she was holding out making me a cup of tea was because she didn't want the window cleaner to see. He tended to come at around 9.45 and she wasn't going to set a precedent by offering him a cup of tea as well.

Mrs Lewis, like the old boy who thought he was singing a top C, is also from what you might call lower down the ladder, though you'd find it harder to detect. A pensioner now, with a war-wounded husband, her cockney accent is only very slight and, through hard work, they've made a good life and home for themselves. It's hard to believe that Ivy, as she lets me call her, lived most of her childhood in an orphanage. When aged five, her father had died in an accident and her mother had been unable to cope with her large brood. Consequently, Ivy and her sister were chosen with great regret to be taken away and looked after in an orphanage. Like so many people who have lived in difficult times, Ivy, a great talker even now, described to me in surprisingly light-hearted tones the harsh conditions of the orphanage. She was apparently a great talker then, and got into constant trouble for being heard as well as seen. The punishment was to spend the day sitting in the corner with a notice cut out in the shape of a large tongue. It would be attached to her back with string, and read: 'My tongue is too large. I must stop talking or it will be cut out!'

What I didn't want to hear from Ivy was the true enactment of what had been practically her lifetime's bad dream. She was late in calling me one year and I half thought she might have passed on, but didn't really want to ring and enquire. When she eventually contacted me she told me why she'd been in hospital. Her nightmarish recurring dream had come true. She'd always feared that one day she would slip on the ice and fall flat on her face, losing her teeth (which she was very proud of). Right enough, it being an icy February, she was nearly home with the shopping when she'd slipped on the pavement and smashed her front teeth. With a badly cut and bruised face, her hip suspected of being broken, she sat on the freezing pavement waiting for help, which eventually came. A spell in hospital put her right. Although she had lost her front teeth in the accident, luckily there were no broken bones. How she could laugh about it with me afterwards I don't know. She did say that it was a relief it was all over now and she'd no more teeth to smash.

The stoicism and wiliness of the older generation! Alas, I'd heard Jim Smith, the Harrods workshop foreman, part of the older craftsmen fraternity along with hammer head Arthur of Camden Town, had apparently died of a heart attack. I knew Arthur had gone: one bout of flu too many. I suppose I wasn't too surprised about Jim, just saddened that another of them had passed on. In fact, I nearly suffered a heart attack myself when I bumped into his lookalike whilst walking along Bournemouth seafront one summer. It was a slightly frailer version, admittedly, but after a second take, we stopped; it *was* him! He greeted me with, "Hello, cod's 'ed, what are you up to these days?" and I enquired not too discreetly after his health. He gave me a quizzical look and then something seemed to click: "Don't tell anyone. I put it around that I'd had a heart attack to stop people ringing me up for French polishing jobs. I've retired now and want to stay that way, so don't go telling anyone where I live!"

10. Have piano, will travel, or time for pastures new?

POSTSCRIPT

So what actually happened to Turner the Tuner? Well, after many years of tuning pianos for the rich, along with a few stars among them, and not forgetting little Miss Harper at Humble Cottage, I retired to the south of France and took up oil painting along the lines of the greats such as Cézanne and Matisse.

Let's get real and come clean. My grandfather, a trained architect, was also a talented artist. My father seemed to inherit the skill too, though had a much greater interest in music and composition (including a few operas). As for me, I've seen eight-year-olds draw better pictures than me, and no, I am not a resident of France. The mention of skilful eight-year-olds is slightly embarrassing, as there have been times when I was expected to teach children art. As much as I enjoyed the independence of being self-employed, the actual process of tuning a piano can be very tedious (although the tediousness can be broken up with time – sometimes days – spent on repairing and renovating pianos). In some ways it could also be a somewhat lonely occupation, as you don't work as part of a team (and, of course, if you are ill and have time off, you don't get paid). Worse still, for the most part it isn't in any way intellectually stimulating.

Tuning pianos in schools, some fairly famous public schools, others run by the local council, gave me an insight into what the modern classroom looked like and how schools operated. On occasion it necessitated meeting with teaching staff, and sometimes working in schools while they were fully functioning with kids and staff present. The conversations with staff, the nostalgia of the classroom, I don't know, that's a job I wouldn't have minded doing had I been smart enough to get the grades… Never mind.

I hadn't officially retired as a piano tuner; some would say I was still relatively young. It would take quite a few years to become a qualified primary school teacher, and I got there eventually, but that's another story.

ACKNOWLEDGEMENTS

Grateful thanks for the kind support, encouragement and cooperation is here recorded to: the British Library; Camden Library Archives; H. J. Fletcher & Newman Ltd; Martin Heckscher FIMIT; Bill Kibby and the Piano History Centre; Institute of Musical Instrument Technology; the Piano Tuners' Association; Yamaha Music UK; Jeremy Thompson FRSA and the publishing team at The Book Guild Ltd.

PICTURE CREDITS